What You Should Know About Alcoholism

What You Should Know About Alcoholism

By DON TRACY

DODD, MEAD & COMPANY   NEW YORK

ISBN: 0-396-06997-5
Library of Congress Catalog Card Number: 74-10007
Printed in the United States of America
by The Cornwall Press, Inc., Cornwall, N. Y.

This book is gratefully dedicated
to the memory of F. R. "Dick" Dickenson,
President, New Life Foundation

Contents

Foreword, 9

O N E :
Identifying the Alcoholic, 17

T W O :
The Alcoholic Behavior, 31

T H R E E :
Alcoholism, the Disease, 43

F O U R :
Myths and Misconceptions About Alcoholism, 51

F I V E :
The Alcoholic Arena, 63

S I X :
Approaching the Alcoholic, 73

S E V E N :
Sources of Effective Help, 93

EIGHT:
Detoxification and Rehabilitation, 115
NINE:
Helping the Alcoholic to Stay Sober and Happy, 133
TEN:
How to Handle the Alcoholic Employee, 151

For Your Information, 157

Foreword

Another book on alcoholism? Who needs it?

Good question. There have been so many books written about alcoholism and the alcoholic that it has half-jokingly been remarked that, as a book topic, problem drinking is running second only to sex, although God knows it's not half as much fun.

Still, with thousands of published words on alcoholism at hand—some brilliantly projected, some scholarly, others incredibly dull—the editors of this book believe there is a void in the area of offering practical, effective help to the alcoholic *through his family, his friends, his business associates, and his employer.*

Let's be realistic. The odds against a man or woman who is half-bombed, totally awash, or in the throes of a hangover picking up a book to read about the alcoholic problem and the ways to deal with it would fracture a tote board. Even if a fearful, remorseful drunk does make the herculean effort, the words blur, the sparkling prose jumbles into gobbledegook, and about three paragraphs are enough to get the book thrown aside while the alcoholic goes in search of a drink to ease his fluttering eyes.

When asked what he thinks of the book that the wife, husband, boss, kids, or the people next door gave him, he says, "Fine. I haven't quite finished it, but from what I've read so far, it ought to be a big help—to anyone who's really hooked on the stuff."

This is not to put down the work done by so many dedicated writers on the alcoholic problem. Doubtless, their books have been of great help to the alcoholic—*after* the victim has faced up to the fact that he or she is a sufferer of this strange and terrible disease, *after* he's stopped drinking long enough to let his eyes and brain and willingness to learn focus on what's offered, *after* the problem drinker has achieved the wonderful understanding that alcoholism is no more shameful than, say, diabetes—although much deadlier.

But what can be done for the alcoholic until that happy day? What can the worried, perplexed, fearful, hurt, angry, compassionate, mostly misinformed family, boss, business associate, or friend do to better understand and help—in positive ways that incur no risk of a disastrous kickback?

That's what this book is all about. If the problem drinker picks it up and reads it, fine. We hope he does, by the dozen, score, and hundred. It will offer him a shortcut to happy sobriety that will save him miles of the rough road he'll travel otherwise. But while we devoutly wish he would seize on this book, absorb its contents, and act on its advice, most of us have gone this route, and experience has told us that he probably won't. Not yet. Maybe never. So it's to you wives, husbands, children, employers, parents, benchmates, buddies, managers, and foremen that this book is mainly addressed. It has been compiled by the editors from the contributions of a volunteer staff of recovered alcoholics and their nonalcoholic spouses, with the help of various medical, psychiatric, sociological, and corporate personnel specialists who are involved with the problem.

This book is the result of the New Life Foundation's concern over the unavailability of practical information on the ways in which nonalcoholics can recognize and help loved ones, friends, and employees stricken with alcoholism. Convinced of the need for such a book, the Foundation appointed an editorial board, which gathered a file of questions most often asked by these concerned people and left unanswered. These questions were studied by the volunteers mentioned above and the answers assembled in *What You Should Know About Alcoholism*.

We believe this book will dispel some of the weird misconceptions that have grown up around the alcoholic and alcoholism, let you nonalcoholics in on the many truths and aids that have too often been considered the recovered alcoholic's privileged information, give you the tools with which to defend yourselves and at the same time help your problem drinker escape the ultimate ravages of the fatal disease of alcoholism.

If at times we seem too lighthearted or even flippant, make no mistake—we know how devastating and frustrating this problem can be. But we know, too, that we are members of the first generation in the history of mankind who have been given the means and the know-how with which to write a happy ending to the suffering alcoholic's tragic story. And we mean *happy*, not just unsuffering.

Don Tracy
for
The New Life Foundation,
St. Petersburg, Florida

Acknowledgments

As the writer whose name is appended to this book, I want to emphasize that I served chiefly as correlator and rewrite man, dealing with information assembled by the New Life Foundation of St. Petersburg, Florida. While I subscribe wholeheartedly to all the facts and opinions included herein, they are not mine; they comprise the input of scores of men and women who answered the New Life Foundation's call for the real nitty-gritty.

The assembling and publication of this book has been part of the New Life Foundation's continuing program of disseminating information about alcoholism to the nonalcoholic. This program supplements the Foundation's other objectives, which include a campaign for improved and more easily accessible detoxification and rehabilitation programs for alcoholics, "troubled employee" programs in the corporate area, education of the general public in the field of alcoholism, research into the alcoholic problem, and other related ranges of practical and theoretical endeavor, including conferences and symposia on the subject of alcoholism.

The trustees of the New Life Foundation, a nonprofit organization, wish to express their deep appreciation to those members of Alcoholics Anonymous, Al-Anon, and other groups concerned with the alcoholic problem who have graciously volunteered their time and experience, without whose enthusiastic cooperation this book could not have been written.

Finally, the New Life Foundation wishes to thank Mr. Frederick R. Dickenson and Dr. Vincent Groupé for serving as associate editors and for gathering the questions and answers which formed the raw material from which the book was written. We also wish to thank Dr. Robert W. Simpson, who showed us the need for this book as well as urged us forward, and Walter W. Hamilton, M.D., for reading the manuscript.

DON TRACY

What You Should Know About Alcoholism

Identifying the Alcoholic

Exactly what is an alcoholic?

There are as many definitions of the word "alcoholic" as there are "experts" to coin them. An all-embracing definition is impossible to come by, but we think the World Health Organization's comes closest: An alcoholic is anyone whose drinking seriously interferes with his or her work, family, social activities, or health.

What is a social drinker?

Here's a loose term that's greatly overworked. Generally, it refers to a person who takes *but does not need* a drink— or several—as part of but not the reason for a social gathering.

Can a social drinker become an alcoholic?

Let's get one thing straight at the start: *Anyone* can become an alcoholic. Alcoholism is no respecter of age, sex, financial standing, education, physical strength, social status, or mental capacity. This is no pantywaist disease we're dealing with here.

Alcoholism is a disease?

Yes. During the past several years, alcoholism has been recognized as a disease—and one of the three worst killer diseases at that—by practically every medical, psychiatric, hospital, and insurance group in the country. It runs third after cardiovascular diseases and cancer. It has generally been branded the number-one health problem in the U.S. It is the undisputed first in the amount of damage it does in all areas—social, economic, political, and criminal.

But alcoholism can be cured, right?

Wrong. But it can be *arrested* and has been in hundreds of thousands of cases, with the recovered alcoholics enjoying happy sobriety in full and purposeful lives.

Are all heavy drinkers alcoholic?

Don't bet the rent, but statistics are very much against the heavy drinker winding up as just a heavy drinker with no alcoholic problem. Until now it's been fashionable to say that a minimal percentage of heavy drinkers escape alcoholism. At the risk of sounding dogmatic, we say that the number of three-martini lunchers and seven-Scotch-on-the-rocks drinkers escaping bad trouble can be stuffed in a gnat's ear.

It stands to reason that a fifth-a-day drinker is more likely to become an alcoholic than a person who takes an occasional short beer. Our experience has been that an appalling percentage of heavy drinkers who boast of their control eventually fall off the razor's edge into alcoholism.

Is there a sure way to tell whether a person is a social drinker or an alcoholic?

If the World Health Organization's definition is a little too indefinite to use at this stage of the game, there have been several tests formulated over the years by Alcoholics Anonymous, the Christopher D. Smither Foundation of New York City, and by Johns Hopkins Hospital in Baltimore, Maryland.

What are these tests?

They're in the form of questionnaires. Probably the most highly regarded is the test originally developed by Johns Hopkins researchers for use in industrial alcoholism programs. Here are the questions you might try on someone you suspect might need help.

Substitute "he" or "she" for the word "you."

1. Do you require a drink the next morning?
2. Do you prefer to drink alone?
3. Do you lose time from work due to drinking?
4. Is drinking harming your family in any way?
5. Do you crave a drink at a definite time daily?
6. Do you get the inner shakes unless you continue drinking?
7. Has drinking made you irritable?
8. Does drinking make you careless of your family's welfare?

9. Have you thought less of your wife or husband since drinking?
10. Has drinking changed your personality?
11. Does drinking cause you bodily complaints?
12. Does drinking make you restless?
13. Does drinking cause you to have difficulty in sleeping?
14. Has drinking made you impulsive?
15. Have you less self-control since drinking?
16. Has your ambition decreased since drinking?
17. Has your initiative decreased since drinking?
18. Do you lack perserverance in pursuing a goal since drinking?
19. Do you drink to obtain social ease? (In shy, timid, self-conscious individuals.)
20. Do you drink for self-encouragement? (In persons with feelings of inferiority.)
21. Do you drink to relieve marked feelings of inadequacy?
22. Has your sexual potency suffered since drinking?
23. Do you show marked dislikes or hatreds since drinking?
24. Has your jealousy, in general, increased since drinking?
25. Do you show marked moodiness since drinking?
26. Has your efficiency decreased since drinking?
27. Has drinking made you more sensitive?
28. Are you harder to get along with since drinking?
29. Do you turn to an inferior environment since drinking?
30. Is drinking endangering your health?
31. Is drinking affecting your peace of mind?
32. Is drinking making your home life unhappy?
33. Is drinking jeopardizing your business—your job?

34. Is drinking clouding your reputation?
35. Is drinking disturbing the harmony of your life?

According to the Hopkins researchers, a yes answer to any question serves as a definite warning that the subject may be an alcoholic. If there is a yes answer to any two questions, chances are that the subject is an alcoholic. Three or more yes answers mean that the subject definitely is an alcoholic.

If a person passes this test with flying colors, does that mean that he or she is safe from alcoholism?

We'd like to say sure, you bet, positively. But there's a big if.

The chances are good *if* the one answering the questions is honest with his or her answers. Sad to say, it's almost certain that a person with a drinking problem will cheat.

That's probably the most baffling symptom of the insidious disease of alcoholism—the alcoholic's gradual, mostly unconscious, surrender to the grimy day-to-day struggle for survival by means of cheating, lying, stealing—anything to protect that bottle of life's blood labeled Old Popskull.

And all the while he fiercely denies that there is a drinking problem.

It's hard to believe that a person with an average or even higher-than-average amount of personal integrity can lie about this one thing, especially to those who love or respect him and want only to help him.

Granted, it's hard, but you'd better believe it! Believe it but don't damn him or her for it, any more than you'd condemn a flu sufferer for running a high fever.

But maybe the one I'm concerned with is different.

Maybe so. Each particular loved one, employee, or friend usually is different in the minds of the people who are disturbed at his or her drinking. One of our staff who has had close contact with thousands of alcoholics, both recovered and lost, puts it this way:

The average "different" American practicing alcoholic is male or female; thin or fat; short or tall; young, old, or middle-aged; white, black, Oriental, Indian, or Eskimo; rich, poor, or of middle income. He or she drinks various kinds of alcoholic beverages on a daily basis or periodically.

He is a professional man, an executive, a businessman, a skilled worker, or a laborer. She is a housewife, a secretary, a nurse, a career woman, or a factory worker.

The alcoholic's drinking habits vary from drinking only beer or wine to a daily consumption of one or two quarts of hard liquor. He or she may or may not drink in the morning, drink at bars or drink at home, alone or in company. Your alcoholic may or may not have hangovers, blackouts, become argumentative, or hide his or her jug to protect the supply.

Almost without exception, the alcoholic *always* denies his or her drinking problem. The alcoholic *always* insists that he or she can stop drinking at any time.

What is the first danger signal of alcoholism?

"Danger signals" differ with different personalities. It's hard to set down a blanket rule. One pretty fair shot is when a man or woman takes a couple of drinks after everybody else at the party has had enough. The "I think I'll have another little touch while you-all are having your coffee" may not be a sure sign, but if this happens more frequently than it does not, something's wrong.

Another fairly reliable sign is a person's decision to have a drink—or two or three—before guests arrive. An almost sure signal is a drinker's resentment of any remark that could be considered a criticism of his or her drinking. When the friendly suggestion that he or she may have been hitting it up a little heavily lately is met with a hurt or angry denial, a "butt out of my business!" response, or a frozen silence, the odds are that the drinker has crossed the line or is pretty close to it.

What line?

The invisible, mysterious demarcation line that separates the alcoholic from the social drinker. This is the point at which the social drinker who has always known that he can quit at any time finds that he can't.

Obviously, most people can drink without ever crossing this line. How do you explain this?

We can't. There's never been a factual explanation found for one person's crossover into compulsive drinking while another with the same background, environment, and drinking history is able to drink socially, under full control, all his or her life.

For what they're worth, scads of theories have been advanced over the years, mentioning allergies, psychological kinks, biochemical lacks and excesses, and so forth. One theory that's gained a certain amount of acceptance is that there's a breakdown or change in the alcoholic's cell structure that sets up a craving for booze at the first taste, at the same time reducing his tolerance for the stuff. But be warned: There are probably more authorities engaged in the study of alcoholism who turn thumbs down on this theory than there are those who subscribe to it.

The important question, so far as we're concerned, is not why it happens but what we can do for the one to whom it does happen.

Are there any other signs to look for?

Dozens, most prevalent among them being the aforementioned denial syndrome. If one characteristic can be confidently ascribed to every alcoholic, it is his instinctive and persistent denial of the problem to the family, to friends, to employers, and, most harmful of all, to himself.

But speaking of looking for signs, let's say a word about examining one's motives in looking for them. They are published here to enable those concerned with the problem drinker to prepare himself or herself for the crash that's coming. To use these signs merely to confirm suspicions that a casual acquaintance is a no-good lush is another game—and a pretty wormy one at that.

Hey, look! I bought the book. What do you want from me, compassion?

At least. Or, if you're not ready for that, at least an attempt to understand what your problem drinker is going through. He or she may break all the rules, insult and outrage you, set fire to the house, wreck the car, wind up in the wrong bed. But it's your job to keep remembering that the alcoholic is suffering from a disease for which he or she is no more to blame in this cocktail-oriented society of ours than the ptomaine victim is to blame for the bad oyster.

Hah! So now it comes out that you're uptight about this "cocktail-oriented society of ours." In other words, this is another treatise on the evils of strong drink.

Not at all. Some of our best friends are social drinkers. As a matter of fact, the writer's wife does a pretty good job on a perfect Rob Roy.

Are there any more danger signals?

In a recent white paper issued by the Criteria Committee of the National Institute on Alcohol Abuse and Alcoholism (NIAAA), published in the *American Journal of Psychiatry* and the *Annals of Internal Medicine,* the following major and minor criteria (diagnostic aids) were listed as being found in the alcoholic.

Minor criteria: cardiac arrhythmia, habits such as gulping drinks, drinking secretly, the occurrence of frequent auto accidents, repeated attempts at abstinence, drinking to relieve pressures or to counteract anger, insomnia, or depression.

Major criteria: presence of the withdrawal syndrome (convulsions or d.t.'s), tolerance of the effects of alcohol, alcoholic blackouts, the daily consumption of a fifth of whiskey or its beer or wine equivalent, continued drinking despite strong medical or social contraindications.

So if a drinker keeps under a fifth of whiskey a day . . .

Whoa! You're about to fasten on a dangerous absolute. Remember, there are no hard and fast rules dealing with this strange and frustrating disease. Or, rather, no positive rule but one:

So long as the alcoholic doesn't take that first drink, he or she won't get drunk.

But getting back to that fifth-a-day figure—while the amount of the daily alcoholic intake is important, of course, even more important is the *way* it's drunk, its effect on the drinker's life, and, above all, the drinker's control over his or her drinking.

In other words, the woman who takes a quick kitchen shot while getting more ice for the party in the front room, the person who gets stiff when he or she has made a self-pledge to go very easy on the drinks for business or social reasons, or the man who drinks a can of beer that he really doesn't want but has to have "to get organized," may all stay far below that fifth-a-day limit and still be in plenty of trouble.

If this is confusing, know that the grim puzzle of alcoholism has baffled some of the world's best minds since the beginning of time. Only in the past few years has there been any progress at all in understanding the problem. Rejoice that you didn't have to try to deal with this forty years ago. Then, there were *no* answers to your questions. Not a one.

How about a bottle hider?

If the problem were not out of control, why would anybody hide a bottle? The bottle-hiding syndrome stems from the alcoholic's fear that somehow the supply will be cut off, leaving him or her gasping for a drink.

The hidden bottle offers security. It also chalks up a score for the alcoholic in his desperate little game against the Opposition, which is comprised of all the people who want him to do something about his drinking. When he has stashed a jug in a new and absolutely unfindable place, the alcoholic has outwitted the enemy. The fact that he has dealt his own self-respect a gut shot doesn't enter into it.

To give an example of the lengths to which an alcoholic will go to protect his supply, take the case of a top executive in a large Eastern corporation who has since recovered. When his home hiding places were discovered, one by one, this wealthy, highly respected corporate executive hied himself to a paint store and bought an empty paint can off the window display. He filled the can with vodka, put a new brush in the lidless can, and left it in full view on his garage workbench. It worked just dandy. There it was, undiscovered, when the men came to carry our hero off to the hospital for another drying-out session.

Does rooting out these hiding places help?

Not much, if at all. We'll go into this later, in the chapter on Approaching the Alcoholic.

What signs of alcoholism in an employee can an employer look for?

Actually, the employer has it much easier than a wife, husband, or friend. He has an irrefutable work record on his desk in front of him. Absenteeism, production drop, and personality clashes with fellow workers or superiors, coming from a heretofore gung ho employee, are made part of the record. It should not take long for any employer who's on the ball to realize that he has a troubled employee on his hands. Surveys show that more than 80 percent of all troubled employees have an alcoholic problem, either their own or their spouse's or another close relative's.

Can a wife recognize alcoholism in her husband—or a husband in his wife—faster than anybody else?

No. The wife is usually the last to admit that her Joe has an alcoholic problem, and the same thing goes for a husband acknowledging that his wife is a problem drinker.

Without getting into the psychological or psychiatric angles, there's an emotional thing involved. Joe doesn't want to admit that Alice is drinking too much because she's lacking something in their relationship, and the same thing goes for the wife. To admit that her husband is seeking something in booze that she can't give him is to admit failure in marriage. For both Joe and Alice to realize that alcoholism is a disease that has nothing to do with love, respect, or physical attraction is the most difficult accomplishment either of them will be called upon to make during their lifetime. "He could quit if he loved me" is the most frequent, most ill-informed statement made these days.   ✓

Lady, if he could quit, he would. Without help of some kind, he can't. Ahead of him lies commitment to an institution, an early grave, or happy sobriety. You can help him achieve the last named. But it will take patience and understanding and, above all, the commitment to the knowledge that you're dealing with a sick person, not a headstrong, self-indulgent, spoiled, reckless, and weak-willed drunk.

Remember that. Keep it always foremost in your mind.

The Alcoholic Behavior

Having read this far, perhaps you've guessed that anyone trying to deal reasonably and intelligently with a practicing alcoholic has a big job on his or her hands. That's true, but let's get another thing straight: It can be done if you care enough—or, in the case of the employer, if the alcoholic worker's past record merits him a chance for survival.

For spouses, friends, and employers, one bit of advice: Try to remember not to come on too heavy; try not to keep too tight a line.

Are you suggesting that the alcoholic be allowed to run loose, with no outside attempts at discipline?

Eventually, by the grace of God, the alcoholic will face up to the fact that without self-discipline (and self-honesty) he cannot survive. But he must reach this conclusion on his own. The record shows that another alcoholic, a *recovered* alcoholic, is the best-qualified person by far to help the problem drinker face this truth. All your threats, tears, and pleading usually do little more than add another few tons to the alcoholic's burden of guilt.

Don't ask why this is so; just take our word for it that that's the way it is.

What's the most baffling symptom of alcoholism?

It's hard to choose one, but if there's a universal trait that's hardest for nonalcoholics to understand, it's the problem drinker's refusal to admit his problem. As one highly regarded authority put it: "Denial is the name of the game."

With the roof caving in on him, with practically everybody else on God's green earth fully aware that he's in deep trouble, with his health, job, family, and bankroll shot to hell, many an alcoholic still manages to cry, "Whaddaya mean, drinkin' problem?"

What's another common trait?

Lying. The alcoholic lies as compulsively as he or she drinks. When a half-empty pint is found in her purse or his pocket, the indignant alcoholic is ready to squawk, "Who put that there—it's not mine!"

Other behavioral traits, please?

Secretiveness, an overwhelming urge to get away from society, dreams of great accomplishment miraculously come by. Also, a disinterest in or aversion to the events of the day. In the later stages of the disease, psychotic fears usually lead into a despair that often has suicidal overtones.

I've heard that an alcoholic's suicide talk is 90 percent self-pity and hot air. Is this right?

Who among us is willing to take a chance on the alcoholic really meaning it this time? Anybody, drunk or sober, who seriously talks suicide should be gotten into a hospital or even a police station as soon as possible.

Statistics on alcoholic suicides are admittedly shaky because of the suicide's family's and friends' efforts to cover up the "stigma" attached to the poor man or woman having been drunk at the time. However, medical, psychiatric, and police experience proves that the incidence of suicide among out-of-control problem drinkers is higher than in all other groups, to a shocking degree.

Does an alcoholic's sexual adventuring really mean anything?

If Joe turns into a Don Juan or Josie into a sexpot only after he or she has taken on a load, chances are that the problem drinker is only trying to reassert his or her desirability. They lack self-assurance; otherwise they wouldn't try to find it in booze. Bear with them and don't let jealousy distort your understanding.

Is the alcoholic a good performer in bed?

About the worst there is.

Instead of letting go and enjoying, the man alcoholic worries about his breath, his virility, and his total lack of interest in women—all women.

The woman alcoholic also worries about the way she

smells, her fading or lost femininity, and her total lack of interest in men—all men.

Somewhere along the line, the bottle has become the only important thing in life. Everything else, even sex, is an aggravating interruption which keeps the alcoholic away from the next drink.

We're speaking of alcoholics now, not people who have to take on a few drinks to shuck their inhibitions.

Well, if most alcoholics don't even enjoy sex, where do they find their fun?

Who's talking about fun? We're discussing the victims of a destructive, fatal disease—not a bunch of fun-loving crazies.

But don't most alcoholics start drinking too much because they find that the more they drink, the more they enjoy?

Yes, many of them do. A great many recovered alcoholics can trace their problem-drinking career back to the time when they never wanted the party to be over. Some built an early tolerance that let them drink everybody else under the table. With liquor, they found their wit sparkling, their appeal to the opposite sex irresistible. They were surrounded by admiring laughter. All the others envied their charm. They had it made, and it was so easily come by—just a few extra drinks! Why didn't everybody else see how simple it was?

The trouble was that these same life-of-the-party types soon discovered that without liquor they were nothing. Of course they exaggerated this difference, and, out of a fear of losing the spotlight, of not getting a full measure of fun out of every moment, of even making somebody *not like them,* they took on ever-increasing quantities of sauce.

Then came the inevitable day when they thought the laughter held a jeering note, when there seemed to be hidden barbs in every half-heard side remark, when the drinker's friends turned against him or her for no reason, out of spite, the ungrateful wretches, the holier-than-thou bastards.

"To hell with 'em," said the lush. Who needed them, anyhow? Let them cut the drinker off the invitation lists; their parties were getting to be a drag, anyway. So he did get into a fight with somebody at the last one (who was that guy?) or she did call her hostess a conniving bitch—didn't they know it was the liquor? Everybody was entitled to one foul-up, wasn't he? Or two, or three?

Finally, it was easier to stay home with a couple of jugs tucked away within easy reach. No aggravations. Then the alcoholic could be sure that he or she was among friends.

This may sound a bit melodramatic, but, actually, it's the tragic story of hundreds of thousands of alcoholics. Many, many others, of course, have no such drinking background. Some progress from a couple of beers at the corner tavern on the way home from work to staying on after their companions have gone home, to occasionally getting drunk on that same bar stool, to being the day's first customer on the way to work, to being unable to make it to work, to losing the job, losing the family, and, finally, losing everything but the compulsion to drink—all at that same friendly neighborhood tavern.

Or there is the wife and mother who starts taking an occasional afternoon drink to relieve the monotony, or the corporation head who seeks relief from "executive tension" in a blast or two on the side, or the lonely widow who gradually increases her sherry input, or the successful sales-man who "has to drink" with his customers to the point where the drinks become important and the customers aren't, or the . . . We could go on and on.

The point is that it's impossible to set down a pre-problem-drinking pattern that would suit every one of this nation's nine million alcoholics.

Nine million?

Approximately, but we'll deal with statistics later.

Would you say that most alcoholics cross that line be-tween social and problem drinking because they think they need liquor to be at their best?

That's a serious oversimplification. A great many do be-cause it's generally agreed that a majority of alcoholics are basically shy, sensitive, and insecure. But there are hun-dreds—thousands—who are anything but shy, sensitive, or insecure, and who were struck down by the disease just as savagely.

Some respected medical authorities lean toward the theory that the physical factors contributing to alcoholism are implanted in the victim at birth. Other, equally re-garded authorities say no, the alcoholic is a personality which fails to mature properly. Still others maintain . . .

But we're not going to get mixed up in that debate.

It's not what *causes* alcoholism that's important; it's what can be done for the alcoholic now, today, before it's too late and the damned disease fills another straitjacket—or another grave.

What is meant by a "periodic drunk"?

This is an alcoholic who is able to go without drinking for varying lengths of time—a month, three months, a year—seemingly without difficulty, and who then falls off the wagon with a disastrous crash. This pattern is repeated, usually with diminishing periods of sobriety, until the alcoholic seeks help, lands in an institution, or dies.

Is that the same as a "binge drinker"?

Not quite. A binge drinker usually is one who doesn't go on the wagon but who keeps the alcoholic intake under control until the day when this control collapses and he or she goes off on a spree.

Which is less dangerous?

That's sort of like asking which is better, carcinoma or leukemia?

I've heard of a problem drinker taking the "geographic cure." What is meant by that?

It's the name given to the familiar alcoholic practice of changing jobs, towns, friends, surroundings, and sometimes mates in the hopes that the factors on which he blames his drinking troubles won't exist in an entirely new situation.

It almost never works simply because the alcoholic takes the main problem—the only real problem—with him wherever he goes. He can never escape it by running. He must face it, acknowledge it, and seek help in grappling with it. It doesn't make a particle of difference where he makes this decision, just so he makes it.

Do you mean to say that an alcoholic bartender or cocktail waitress shouldn't find another line of work?

Changing jobs, alone, will not solve the alcoholic bartender's or cocktail waitress's drinking problem. However, once he or she has decided to face and do something about the problem, getting out from among all those bottles and glasses and liquor breaths should make the way back to happy sobriety that much less rugged.

And just to keep the record straight, the AA rolls include many recovered alcoholics who "made the program" while working as bartenders and cocktail waitresses. While we may admire them for doing it the hard way, there are few among us who can recommend it.

Can the alcoholic regain control of his or her drinking by changing the drinks? Switching from whiskey to light wine, say, or from vodka to beer?

No way. If the government had a dollar for every time this has been tried unsuccessfully, none of us would have to worry about the national debt.

Do alcoholics drop their former friends and associates because they find themselves liking only other alcoholics?

Alcoholics don't really like anybody, not even themselves. They tend to gravitate to other alcoholics simply because they can be fairly sure that in their company they won't be criticized for getting drunk. But even here, the alcoholic must feel that he or she is not in as bad shape as the others—*they* may all be hooked on booze but not *this* baby! The moment there's the least doubt of his or her superiority, the alcoholic either seeks other drinking companions who are obviously further down the road or becomes a solitary drinker.

To the lone drinker, the "benefits" of solitary drinking include the absence of comparisons and freedom from unwelcome glimpses of what lies ahead. Also, he or she can feel free to believe that the problem is being kept completely hidden from the outside world.

But surely there must be some happy *drunks among these nine million alcoholics!*

In the early stages, yes, we suppose so, depending on your definition of happiness. In the later stages, no, nothing but misery and despair. Life-savoring Elwood P. Dowd and his giant rabbit, Harvey, made a swell play and movie, but the most unrealistic part of the script wasn't the king-sized bunny but Elwood's happy, rose-colored haze of alcoholism.

Is the reason that an alcoholic hurts his family and the close friends and/or employers who least deserve it because he or she is releasing true, deep-seated, pent-up feelings?

No, that old *in vino veritas* aphorism doesn't hold true for the alcoholic, because during the course of the disease he or she undergoes a personality change that first distorts, then cripples, and eventually destroys his or her true self.

During this deterioration, the alcoholic becomes so confused and frightened at what is happening that he or she lashes out blindly in desperate, if futile, efforts to ward off the enemy. The ones who invariably get hurt the worst by this are those closest to the alcoholic. They're the most pitiful "innocent bystanders" of the disease.

What about the old saying that a man has to get drunk with another to really know him?

Baloney! You might as well say that you find out what a person's really like only when he's out of his head with fever—or when he's just shot up on heroin.

In looking over the foregoing questions and answers on alcoholic behavior, I've found nothing that exactly fits the person with whom I'm concerned.

As somebody must have once said, let us make one thing perfectly clear: There are almost as many different alcoholic behavioral patterns as there are alcoholics. Underlying each of them, however, is the emerging indication of the drinker's life becoming unmanageable. That's the behavioral norm.

There's an old saying in Alcoholics Anonymous that

puts it this way: If you listen to enough stories told by recovered alcoholics, you'll eventually hear one that is *exactly* your own story, almost word for word. As exaggerated as this may seem, it's absolutely true.

Alcoholism, the Disease

Just how widespread is alcoholism in this country?

According to a recent special report issued by the Department of Health, Education, and Welfare, about 7 percent of the adult population of the United States is afflicted with the disease of alcoholism. Roughly figuring the adult population at 140 million, this would total 9.8 million alcoholics in the U.S. However, the HEW estimate allowed for X number of hidden alcoholics and those suffering from physical and mental illnesses that might be traceable to alcoholism. The more accepted estimates put the number of alcoholics in this country at 9 million.

What's the percentage of alcoholics among those who drink?

HEW estimates that two-thirds of all Americans drink, so that adult drinking is "normal" behavior in our society. Of these drinkers, almost 10 percent will cross that invisible line into alcoholism.

Is alcohol an addiction?

Yes, like heroin, addiction to alcohol is characterized by dependence, an increase in tolerance, and the onset of withdrawal symptoms when the victim is deprived of alcohol. Unlike heroin, alcohol addiction usually develops slowly and insidiously over a period of years. In addition, the tolerance developed for alcohol is less dramatic than that observed in the heroin or morphine addict. Perhaps a little-known fact is that withdrawal from alcohol is *more dangerous* than withdrawal from heroin because of the frequency of alcoholic convulsions.

What are the medical complications of alcoholism?

Brain damage and cirrhosis of the liver are pretty well-known by-products of uncontrolled drinking. Not so well known, perhaps, is the fact that almost every alcoholic suffers from malnutrition, a condition that opens hell's own toy box of physical ailments. The nourishing food intake of most alcoholics wouldn't keep a gnat healthy. What he does manage to choke down is poorly absorbed, and, on top of that, alcohol produces a condition (diuresis) that "washes out" water-soluble vitamins.

A medical list of alcoholism-induced maladies includes malnutrition, cirrhosis of the liver, neuropathy, destruction of nerve tissues, increased heartbeat, lowered resistance to infection, pancreatitis, anemia, respiratory ailments, and cardiac abnormalities.

Are there as many women alcoholics as men?

No, although the margin appears to be narrowing. One of the more widely accepted statistics places the male–female ratio at five to three (in 1950 it was set at *six to one!*), but as with most statistics dealing with alcoholism, it's open to argument.

While it's a fact that more women drink socially today than used to, some authorities think the increase in the female alcoholic figures is at least partly due to the steady erosion of the stigma factor. Time was, and not so long ago, when a woman with an alcoholic problem was somehow immoral. Nowadays, more and more women alcoholics are facing the problem and seeking help. In other words, the true male–female percentages are just now beginning to be known.

Can people who drink only beer become alcoholic?

Certainly, why not? It's the alcohol and not the form it's in that counts. Most alcoholics "graduate" to hard liquor because it's quicker than beer—and some later turn to wine because it's cheaper—but there have been thousands upon thousands who have stuck with beer to the bitter end.

Why is alcoholism called a progressive disease?

Because it keeps on getting worse, even when the alcoholic stops drinking. If an alcoholic stops drinking and maintains total abstinence for, say, ten years and then resumes drinking, the force of compulsion does not take up at the point where he or she stopped. Instead, the booze returnee finds himself much more helpless than ten years ago. His former tolerance for alcohol has disappeared. The slide into alcoholic chaos is dreadfully swift.

Nobody builds up "good time" against alcoholism by staying sober awhile, no matter how long he abstains. It will *never* be safe for him to take another drink, even a short beer.

Remember, alcoholism is never cured; it can only be arrested. We ordinarily don't like scare stories, but here's a true one that might give you an idea: A man with eight years of solid sobriety in Alcoholics Anonymous decided that it wouldn't hurt if he had a glass of champagne at his daughter's wedding reception. Three weeks later, he came to in the psycho ward of a hospital some three hundred miles away.

No, of course it wasn't that one glass of wine that put him there. But the champagne was the *first* drink that no alcoholic can take.

Is alcoholism inherited?

There are no proven facts that say so. However, it may be fair to assume that a person surrounded by the same social and economic conditions under which his father or mother or both became alcoholics might be more susceptible than that legendary creature, the "average person."

What is the annual loss in dollars and cents due to the disease of alcoholism?

The total loss in all areas is impossible to estimate. Recent Public Health Service estimates of the loss *to industry alone* placed the figure at more than $15 billion a year.

Is strict early home training an effective deterrent to alcoholism?

Not necessarily. As many recovered alcoholics say they turned to booze in rebellion against strict parental control as came from alcoholic households where there was almost no home training. The great majority seem to have been brought up in "average" homes where training was neither too strict nor too permissive.

However, here we're getting into the sociologist's and child psychologist's field, where any angel with good sense fears to tread.

Why is there a social stigma placed upon alcoholism?

Let's use the word *was* instead of *is,* for starters. Granted, the misinformed or uninformed among us still sneer when they say the word "alcoholic," but their numbers are steadily dwindling. Recognition of alcoholism as a disease, education of the coming generations in the true facts about alcoholism, our honest facing up to the problem, and it is to be hoped the lifting of the last hypocritical cover-ups will erase the last traces of undeserved stigma. And in our lifetime.

As to why the stigma, alcoholism is basically an anti-social disease. Its victims seem compelled to break all the established rules of "polite society." So long as these misdeeds were considered the work of weak, willful, immoral misfits, it's little wonder that a stigma was put on them. Actually, they deserved it even less than they deserved the occasional excuse to the effect that "drink is a good man's failing."

Why are women alcoholics more maligned than their male counterparts?

We're not sure that alcoholics, either men or women, are actually maligned too often in this day and age. Misunderstood, ostracized, unloved, given up on, yes, but "maligned" connotes a certain vicious reaction that is becoming increasingly rare.

If you ask why it is sometimes harder for the nonalcoholic to accept a woman's alcoholism than a man's, we can only offer that it must be an echo from the dim, not so distant past when the only women who were seen drinking in public (except champagne at Delmonico's or beer at the Turnverein) were (blush) ladies of the evening.

Is this double standard changing?

The ones about whom we can speak with authority on this point are the people in Alcoholics Anonymous and other recovery programs. Among AAs, at least, the common problem is alcohol and there is *no* difference in the welcome, acceptance, and shared help offered a woman who wants to stop drinking from that offered a man. If there ever was a double standard here, it didn't last long.

Is the fact that alcoholism is a disease really being accepted generally?

Yes, in medical, psychiatric, hospital, insurance, and other professional circles, including the military. There are certain exceptions, of course. There are bound to be with such an insidious, mysterious, complex problem—but the dissenters in the professional field comprise only a relative handful.

Among the general public there is still a lot of educational work to be done, but universal acceptance of the fact that alcoholism is a disease is definitely on its way.

Do some physicians refuse to treat alcoholics, and if so, why?

The second part of your question gives the answer to the first part: Yes, there are still many physicians who say "Thanks, but no thanks" when an admitted problem drinker asks the doctor to take his case.

Reasons for this are many and varied. Some physicians still hold to the belief that alcoholism is strictly a psychiatric problem, out of their field. However, we believe that the main reason is that since the beginning of medical history, alcoholic patients have proven to be the rudest, crudest, most unreliable, undependable, dishonest, frustrating, and downright untreatable men and women on the books. Physicians are only human, after all, and few welcome an involvement that has a one-in-a-thousand chance of scoring a successful result under medical treatment alone.

With the gradual and sadly overdue development of medical school teaching on the subject, plus the steady increase in the individual physician's interest in the disease of alcoholism, the future promises the doom of the old "he's a lush; give him the brush" principle.

Is there any indication of a breakthrough in research that will lead to some wonder drug which will wipe out alcoholism?

No.

But with the huge sums being spent . . .

Hold it, please. Considering the enormity of the problem and compared to the sums spent on other diseases, the money being directed to the alcoholic problem is a tiny drop in a big bucket. It sometimes seems that whenever government looks around for a budget to slash, the first one it hits is the one that's concerned with the alcoholic problem.

Using round figures, there are at least 100 persons suffering from alcoholism to every person stricken with cancer. Yet for every dollar budgeted for programs dealing with the problem of alcoholism, more than $100 is budgeted for cancer research. Still, according to the Surgeon General, alcoholism is America's number-one health problem. Why, then, doesn't it get a fair shake at funding time?

Then it's just a question of not enough money for research that's holding up the solution to the problem of alcoholism?

We didn't say that. While studies of biological addiction are always good, we have doubts that a miracle drug to cure or prevent alcoholism will ever be found. We believe the present funding needs to be more in the area of extension and improvement of detoxification and rehabilitation services.

CHAPTER FOUR

Myths and Misconceptions About Alcoholism

All modern-day enlightened sympathy aside for the moment, isn't it a fact that most alcoholics get that way because they lack good old-fashioned willpower?

No, absolutely not. Of all the wrong ideas about the disease of alcoholism, the "no willpower" accusation is the most common and the most fallacious. Furthermore, nonalcoholics probably have the greatest trouble accepting the fact that willpower has little or nothing to do with alcoholism.

Some of the strongest-willed people in history have become alcoholics—statesmen, government leaders, business tycoons, generals, admirals, sports heroes, university presidents, leading feminists—you name it. These were men and women who attained the top rung of the ladder in careers that demanded high-level, disciplined exertion of their

51

wills over others, and yet they were destroyed by this disease as tragically as the most weak-willed nobody.

Alcoholism's contemptuous triumph over willpower is one of the most devastating symptoms of the disease. It is also one of the biggest stumbling blocks that prevent the alcoholic from admitting his problem. Far too many sick people are getting sicker and sicker because they hang onto the thought that while they don't seem to have enough willpower to stop drinking at the moment, they're working on it, and tomorrow . . .

Again, we repeat: Willpower or the lack of it has nothing to do with the disease of alcoholism.

Does alcoholism run in the family?

We've known alcoholics whose parents, sisters, brothers, grandparents, cousins, uncles, and aunts were all problem drinkers. We've also known many, many alcoholics whose folks used alcohol in moderation and whose family trees didn't have another tosspot. And the alcoholics who have come from strict teetotaler homes are almost as numerous as those in the other two groups.

Can the love of a good woman make an alcoholic straighten up and fly right?

Only if she directs her love (and understanding and patience and fortitude) to helping him face his problem and in making it as easy as possible for him to seek help.

The fond hope that he's going to change his drinking pattern—"reform"—simply because he marries her or moves in with her is doomed from the start and it has been every time it's been cherished, alas and alack!

Does it take a woman less time than a man to become an alcoholic?

According to figures supplied by the National Instittute of Alcoholism and the Abuse of Alcohol (NIAAA), more men suffer serious alcohol-related problems between the ages of 21 and 24 than at any other age. Relatively few women, on the other hand, suffer from severe alcohol-related problems when in their twenties. The bulk of such problems seems to hit them in their thirties and forties.

These statistics, like all others, are influenced by many varying factors. For instance, young men have far more opportunities for hard drinking than do young women—men get earlier and faster starts. Even in these enlightened times, a woman who gets falling-down drunk turns off prospective dates and husbands, and she knows this. It's usually not until after she's married and has started a family that she lets herself give in to her alcoholic tendencies.

Then, as we said earlier, a woman is better at hiding her alcoholic sickness than a man. It may well be that more women than the NIAAA figures show are in trouble in their twenties but manage to suppress the signs until they get too bad to hide, in their thirties.

I've heard that an alcoholic goes through his or her worst time when the moon is full. Is this true?

We hate to explode a myth that's been around for ages, but there's no available proof that the moon has anything to do with alcoholism.

Perhaps we'd better hedge a bit on that: If an alcoholic is convinced that he has to drink more during a full moon, he can psych himself into a stepped-up compulsion with no trouble at all. But the same "reasons" for drinking have been given rainy days, holidays (including St. Swithin's Day), sunny days, paydays, idle-handed days, overbusy days —you name it.

Is it true that anyone who has passed the age of fifty without becoming an alcoholic is "home free"?

While statistics show a downward curve in the incidence of alcoholism among men and women in their fifties and beyond, the "home free" dictum is far too sweeping.

Thousands of men have been hit by alcoholism after their retirement. Many a woman has been struck down after her children have grown up and left home and she has found time hanging heavy on her hands. The stresses of the menopause have been named as factors sometimes contributing to alcoholism. Widows and widowers, their spouses taken from them late in life, sometimes turn to alcohol to ease their grief and loneliness.

Alcoholism respects a person's age no more than it does any other aspect of the human condition. While the warning signs of the disease usually appear before the potential victim's fifties, alcoholism can strike at any age.

As appalling as the spread of drug abuse among our young people is, I've heard that it has virtually banished real or incipient alcoholism among our youth, particularly on the college campus.

As with all campus enthusiasms and turnoffs, the situation is apt to change without notice, but *at this writing* the move is away from the drug scene and back to booze. Across the land, educators are increasingly worried about the rise in alcohol-related incidents among their students.

Lest this book begin to sound like a temperance tract, which it's not, let us hasten to say that an increase in drinking among students does not mean a flood of young full-blown or on-the-way alcoholics are coming off the campuses ipso facto. There are many who will argue that it's better that a young person risk alcoholic addiction rather than drug addiction when they join the action on the campus. You'll never hear anything like "better drugs than booze" from this corner, but, at the same time, we'd be remiss if we didn't point out that the proven percentages show that the more people there are who drink, the more alcoholics emerge.

One brighter note should be sounded here: Today's youth is much better informed about the facts of alcoholism than his parents, although there's still much to be done in this field. Also, by and large, today's students are more prone to act on such information, as it concerns them as individuals, rather than keeping on with booze against their better judgment just to avoid being different from the rest of the herd.

If I've been told once, I've been told a hundred times that alcoholism is always the symptom of some deep-seated mental problem, never the problem itself. How about it?

Any successful, long-term alcoholic rehabilitation program includes moves toward helping the patient know himself, be honest with himself, and face reality with a certain measure of confidence in his ability to cope without alcohol. In Alcoholics Anonymous, for instance, it is suggested that the new member take a searching and fearless inventory of himself when he has acquired a certain amount of sobriety and feels up to it. These inventories invariably uncover hangups that the alcoholic has kept hidden from himself, and some of these are deep-seated indeed.

That these problems contributed to the victim's alcoholism is undeniable. However, the old theory that the mental problem is the main concern and that the alcoholism is only a symptom is being increasingly debated.

It used to be claimed that when the mental problem was exposed, the alcoholic symptoms would clear up, but that method of treatment never turned in much of a track record, as most psychiatrists would freely admit. Today's more successful procedures play it the other way around, arresting the alcoholism first and then helping the alcoholic take a good, honest look at himself so he can expose his own hidden hangups and work at ridding himself of them.

Always keeping foremost in his mind that one great truth: *I cannot drink.*

In our society, when a person admits to being an alcoholic and seeks help, does he or she risk a future of side-glances, sniggers, whispers, and being the butt of bum jokes, if not virtual ostracism?

First, the practicing alcoholic usually is side-glanced, sniggered at, whispered about, and made the butt of bum jokes, if not ostracized, so even if this were true, what would he have to lose except his misery?

But, of course, it's not true. All misapprehensions to the contrary, the man who faces the problem and seeks help invariably finds to his total amazement that everybody who counts is behind him 100 percent. That goes double for the woman who finally reaches the decision to "do something" about her drinking.

This is a flat promise, one of the very few to be found in this book.

We said "everybody who counts," because occasionally there might be a former boozing buddy or five-martini lunch companion who will try to give the nondrinker a hard time. But as one reenters the world of the living, what the stay-behinds do or say becomes increasingly unimportant.

Doesn't a self-admitted alcoholic sacrifice his chances of being given added responsibility in his position or on his job?

Quite the contrary. Almost without exception, an employer's regard for and confidence in an employee is strengthened by the knowledge that he or she has faced up to the problem that, in most cases, was no secret to the alcoholic's superiors and co-workers. When sobriety brings increased efficiency and dependability, plus improved interpersonal relations, as it must, what employer could help but take advantage by giving the nondrinking alcoholic more responsibility?

Just to keep the record straight, we must admit to having heard of a scant handful of bosses (straight out of the Dark Ages) who still mutter: "I could never trust a man who doesn't take a drink." About all we can say about this breed is that any man or woman, alcoholic or not, would be better off working for somebody else.

Is it true that the F.B.I. has a file on every known alcoholic in the U.S.?

No, not unless the alcoholic has tangled with the law or has let himself be conned into membership in a subversive organization—and that goes for all of us.

What about the comment I've heard: "If So-and-so ever stops drinking, the shock to his nervous system will probably kill him."?

This comment would be almost funny if it weren't, in fact, criminal. In effect, it proposes that a man must continue on a course that will surely kill him because to try to escape this fate might kill him.

Stopping drinking is never any picnic for the alcoholic. But modern medicine has perfected detoxification treatment to the point that withdrawal discomfort is considerably reduced.

I've heard certain people say that for an alcoholic to find sobriety in AA and then devote his off-the-job life to AA is merely substituting one crutch for another. Please comment on this?

One of our AA acquaintances answered this doozy with a simple: "At least I can live happily with this crutch."

Be honest now: Isn't the life of a nondrinking alcoholic one long drag?

It sure can be, unless the recovered alcoholic finds something to fill the vacuum created by the removal of liquor from his life. Almost any alcoholic who has stopped drinking on his own will attest to the fact that he may have been dry but he sure didn't enjoy it.

That's why the fellowship aspects offered by Alcoholics Anonymous have played such an important part in AA's unparalleled success. AA offers friends, understanding, laughter, and unbounded opportunity to fill that vacuum with meaningful activity. More about this later.

If a person with alcoholic tendencies can be persuaded to change his or her lifestyle so that the conditions and companions that caused the overdrinking are removed, wouldn't that help?

This sounds like the old "geographical cure" mentioned earlier, more nicely put. First, the conditions and the companions didn't cause the overdrinking. The alcoholic crossed over the line; he was not dragged across.

We suppose there have been alcoholics who stopped drinking in new surroundings—at least for a time—but in the overwhelming majority, they found new drinking companions and created new conditions almost identical with those they left behind in the move to greener pastures.

Again, the alcoholic carries his problem with him wherever he goes, with whomever he deals.

If Skid Row inhabitants account for such a small percentage of the alcoholic population, why are they given so much exposure by some agencies dealing with the alcoholic problem?

We think it's lamentable that some well-meaning people have publicized the Skid Row derelict to show the depths to which the ravages of alcoholism have carried some men and women. In our estimation, such misdirected publicity has given countless other suffering alcoholics the chance to say: "I'm nothing at all like those poor bums; therefore I can't be an alcoholic."

The only explanation we can give for the occasional overemphasis on the Skid Row drunk is the nonalcoholic ad man's use of the dramatic shock factor in his campaign. The "average" alcoholic offers no such dramatic picture. For him or her, it's a dreary, desperate, soul-grinding process, hidden under the shoddy armor of persistent denial.

Haven't you ever heard of a **happy** *drunk?*

Happy drunks, yes; happy alcoholics in the late stages, no. Without exception, the recovered alcoholic can tell you that at some point along the way, all the fun went out of drinking.

I have it on good authority that if you drink only well-aged whiskey that has little or no fusel oil, you will run very little risk of becoming an alcoholic.

Tell your "good authority" to check again. Chemical analysis has proved that the concentration of fusel oils in whiskey actually *increases* with aging. And there is no known relationship between fusel oil content and alcoholism.

The Alcoholic Arena

You've said that an alcoholic is just like any other person, only more so, but aren't there some people who are more prone to alcoholism than others?

Yes, the overall alcoholic rate among American Indians is twice the national average. The Public Health Service has reported that among American Indians, the majority of suicides, murders, accidental deaths, and injuries are associated with drinking, as are cases of infection, cirrhosis of the liver, and malnutrition. In addition, 76 percent of all fines, arrests, and imprisonments among American Indians result from drinking.

Why is this so?

Nobody knows.

How about blacks?

To be frank, there are few reliable figures dealing with the alcoholism rate among blacks. For years it was generally assumed that although the inebriation rate among low-income blacks was very high, with its resultant job and police problems, the incidence of true alcoholism among them was really quite low.

Recently, researchers have been taking a closer look as communication with the black community improves, slowly but steadily.

What percentage of all alcoholics are Skid Row derelicts?

A Department of Health, Education, and Welfare report offers the following breakdown:

Men and women who are usually still married and living with their families, still holding a job—often an important one—and still are accepted and reasonably respected members of their community account for more than 70 percent of all alcoholics.

Impoverished "homeless" men who usually no longer have, or never did have, family ties, jobs, or an accepted place in the community—the Skid Row alcoholics—account for 3 to 8 percent of all alcoholics.

Mentally ill patients, usually in state hospitals, with a severe chronic psychosis may account for 5 to 10 percent of all alcoholics.

However, these statistics, while interesting and informative in a study of the general problem, don't really mean a whole hell of a lot to the individual alcoholic or to those who are hurt by the side effects. Alcoholism can strike anywhere, at any time, and when it strikes, the fact that the victim does or does not conform to the charts is neither a comfort nor an aid in meeting the problem.

Is alcoholism a rich man's disease or a poor man's burden?

Neither. According to every reliable survey, it takes its greatest toll among members of our so-called "upper middle class."

We don't want to be unduly repetitive but these figures, too, may be misleading. It stands to reason that the wealthy alcoholic is "protected" from outside recognition (and help) far more than the person of moderate means or the low-income victim. Alcoholics Anonymous is not overcrowded with multimillionaires—although there are more AAs in the upper tax brackets than you might suppose.

Generally speaking, the very wealthy alcoholic is to be found in a plush sanitarium where he or she is "suffering from nervous exhaustion" and being pampered by well-meaning (we hope) doctors who assure the patient that drinking is only a symptom, never the cause of the problem.

Is there as high a rate of alcoholism among men and women in the professions—law, medicine, education, and the clergy—as in other walks of life?

Yes, higher. As a matter of fact, recent studies have proved that as a group clergymen are the hardest hit of all.

Until fairly recently, these doctors, lawyers, teachers, ministers, and priests were closely protected by their colleagues, who took the attitude that they had to "take care of our own dirty linen." With the knowledge that alcoholism is a disease, not a shameful failing, more and more members of the professions are facing the problem and seeking help in exactly the same ways as the auto mechanic, the department store clerk, the housewife, and the farm-hand.

Are creative people such as artists, writers, and actors especially vulnerable to alcoholism?

Men and women whose life work is dedicated to fantasy, imaginative exploration, and make-believe too often use alcohol to rev up their talent when they feel it is sagging. Temperamentally, they're less fitted to cope with stress, discouragement, or frustration than those whose jobs keep them in closer touch with reality. Highly individualistic, more often than not egocentric, unhappily they're also great ones for self-pity, an almost ever-present fear of not being appreciated enough. All these traits combine to give them a glass chin when alcoholism takes a swing at them.

If the artist, the writer, and the actor is a patsy for alcoholism, does that mean that the unskilled laborer or the woman who never made it through high school is safer from the disease?

No. Remember, the higher rate of alcoholics among artists was figured on a *percentage* basis, so many alcoholics per hundred writers, actors, etc. The statistics concerning this special group do not affect the overall percentages, which include victims in all walks of life and with all sorts of financial, educational, and family backgrounds.

Is there such a thing as a typical alcoholic?

Not really, any more than there is a typical American. As noted earlier, the more the scientists go to their computers, the more proof they get that "an alcoholic is just like anybody else, only more so."

NIAAA, in a recent survey directed at putting to rest the Skid Row bum image, found that more than 70 percent of the known alcoholics studied lived in respectable neighborhoods, lived with their husbands or wives, tried to send their children to college, paid taxes, and continued to perform more or less effectively in a wide range of positions; there were bank presidents, salesmen, farmers, machinists, stenographers, teachers, clergymen, and physicians.

That same survey, incidentally, came up with the rather startling word that *fewer than 45 percent* of the men on New York's Bowery could be definitely labeled alcoholic. More than 55 percent of those studied in that particular Skid Row were moderate or nondrinkers.

My cousin, the student, has mentioned the Jellinek Classification. What is it?

It is the result of a study made some time ago by the late E. M. Jellinek, the highly respected professor of physiology at Yale University who was a pioneer in scientific investigation into the field of alcoholism.

According to the Jellinek Classification, most alcoholics are included in five main groups, Alpha, Beta, Gamma, Delta, and Epsilon. To go into all the groups in any depth not only would be space-consuming but would serve no purpose here. Suffice it to say that the vast majority of alcoholics in the U.S. come under the Gamma classification. Their illness includes loss of control in drinking, physical dependence on alcohol, increased tolerance to booze, a steady progression of the disease, withdrawal from interpersonal relationships, persistent denial of a problem, etc.

Ninety-nine and forty-four hundredths percent of the recovered alcoholics in AA are Gamma alcoholics.

Is it true that teenagers rarely become alcoholics?

Alcoholic addiction takes longer to develop than drug addiction and therefore full-blown teenage alcoholics are relatively uncommon. But they are not unknown. And the drinking patterns that can lead to alcoholic addiction are often formed during the victim's teens. That's why awareness of the problem of alcoholism at the junior high and high school levels is so important.

Are some alcoholics harder to reach (in an effort to help) than others?

First, let's emphasize again that for help to be effective the alcoholic must face up to the need for help himself. Efforts to help which are attempted before this "bottom" or moment of truth has been reached must be carefully handled lest they be misdirected, causing the sick person to back off and raise defenses that might delay or impair this all-important decision.

With this fact in mind, it's fair to say that some alcoholics who desperately need help are slower to face up to the truth than others. These include the very wealthy, those whose business, professional, or social successes have not yet visibly deteriorated because of their alcoholism, those who are overprotected by loyal subordinates or by family or friends who refuse to admit there is a problem, those afflicted with an overdose of false pride, religious fanatics, and those who for one reason or another have no real interest in living.

Does a person's religious training or lack of it play any part in his or her susceptibility to alcoholism?

A scan of a thousand or so recovered alcoholics indicates that the vast majority were given what might be termed a "normal" amount of religious training in their childhood and teens, with only a sprinkling coming from nonreligious or antireligious families.

Almost without exception, they said that their religious values went to pot, along with all their other higher-plane values, as the disease progressed. Those who had clung to their religious beliefs generally agreed that in the later stages of alcoholism they felt that "God doesn't listen to drunks."

Can a highly spiritual person become an alcoholic?

We can only refer you to the earlier statistics which showed that as a group Catholic priests and Protestant clergymen have a very high alcoholism rate.

Can the wife of a problem drinker or the husband of an alcoholic wife be carried "over the line" by the mate's uncontrolled drinking?

In the case of an alcoholic couple, one invariably blames the other for his or her drinking. And it is true that if a person has alcoholic tendencies, living with an alcoholic spouse encourages the full and rapid development of those tendencies. But just how many husbands and wives are carried "over the line" against their natural inclinations is open to question.

Not that it hasn't happened, perhaps more times than the figures indicate.

One such case that comes to mind concerns the wife of a highly successful politician in one of the Middle Atlantic states who valiantly tried to cope with her husband's alcoholism for twenty years or more and finally "just got tired," as she put it. On the strength of the old adage, "If you can't beat 'em, join 'em," she started drinking and wound up a basket case in a shockingly brief span of weeks —liver damage, d.t.'s, broken bones caused by drunken falls—the works. Worst of all, the husband finally went to AA and started back on the road to recovery, but, so far as we know, the wife never did.

Is the alcoholic business executive in a more difficult situation than the working stiff with a drinking problem?

Not really, although he's very apt to think he is. Too often his position of power and responsibility makes it hard for him to admit he has a problem which he can't take care of on his own.

If he does admit it, the idea of seeking help from recovered alcoholics who may not be anywhere close to him in earnings or status, as in Alcoholics Anonymous, sometimes raises another high hurdle. Private sanitariums and drying-out joints which specialize in "executive tension" treatment have been getting fat off these cases for years.

However, experience has shown that once the executive fully understands what he's up against—a disease, not a lack of willpower—he usually directs the drive that made him successful in the business world toward achieving and maintaining sobriety.

Not long ago the president of a nationally known manufacturing company, an affiliate of a huge conglomerate, found himself on the brink of despair because of his "secret" drinking. Deciding he had to resign before he wrecked his company and exposed his "weakness," he went to the top man of the conglomerate and said: "I've got something terrible to tell you." The big boss replied: "Do you mean you're finally going to do something about your drinking?"

Happy ending: The company president went to AA at the big boss's urging—although at first he drove thirty miles each way to attend meetings where he'd be sure he wouldn't be recognized—and achieved comfortable and long-lasting sobriety.

Are women alcoholics basically different from men alcoholics?

We should hope so, and *vive la différence!*

Seriously, there are certain differences between the two on both the plus and minus side, so far as recovery is concerned. In some circles, the woman alcoholic is still faced with the last tattered shreds of the old stigma bugaboo which the man escapes by and large. Her misguided concern about what the neighbors would think if they knew she had an alcoholic problem is rarely shared by the man alcoholic. He usually despises the neighbors anyway. The woman alcoholic is sometimes burdened by guilt over her real or imagined failure to be a good mother to her children. While the man often worries about not being a good father, it is seldom to the mother's degree. The woman is usually less able than the man to put possible alcohol-related romantic adventures in their proper perspective. When she embarks on a course of recovery, she may have more trouble than the man in forgiving herself for things she did or did not do when she was drinking.

On the plus side of the ledger, the woman alcoholic has no he-man image to try to preserve. She can accept help without feeling she has somehow let herself down, without the thought that she lacks the guts to tough it out by herself. A woman's concern about what her alcoholism is doing to her face and figure is often the deciding factor that makes her admit she has a problem, whereas most men couldn't care less. Also, women alcoholics seem to accept the fact that they are suffering from a disease more readily and to follow the prescribed treatment to arrest that disease.

Approaching the Alcoholic

What's the most important "must" a person should consider when trying to help somebody who has a drinking problem but won't admit it?

If there's a number-one *must*, it's that the person who's trying to help must convince the alcoholic that he or she is on the problem drinker's side.

Is that so difficult?

Yes, it's a lot easier said than done. At the first mention of his drinking problem, the alcoholic is almost sure to go on the defensive in varying degrees of hostility, depending on the degree to which the disease has progressed. You should be ready for the flat denial that there is any problem, accusations of disloyalty and holier-than-thou-ism, of exaggerating the situation, of plain nagging, and, finally, of having gone over to the enemy for dark and devious reasons.

Almost without exception, the alcoholic will swear that he or she can stop drinking without outside help. The suffering alcoholic's most frequent cry is: "I can handle this myself." Another is: "Let me sweat this bad one out and I promise you that things will be different from now on." Or even: "I've had it! Never again!"

When he's reminded that he's said the same thing before when he's been in the throes of a hangover and surveying the damage his drinking has caused him, he'll probably say: "I know, but this time I mean it."

And he does, with all his heart—at the time. With a pounding head and churning stomach, full of remorse over the things he can remember doing, scared to death of what he might have done that he *can't* remember, he (and, of course, this goes for the woman problem drinker, too) really believes that enough is enough; he'll never touch another drop, no matter what. Or at least no more drinks after he's had a couple of "medicinal" drams to quiet his shrieking nerve ends.

Then a good time to approach the alcoholic is when he or she is suffering from a hangover?

Not if he or she is in such bad shape that medical attention is needed. Trying to talk to a person who's on the verge of alcoholic convulsions is not only useless, it's dangerous.

When can the alcoholic best be approached?

When he finally admits he's had it. Then, ideally, the alcoholic should be brought face-to-face with his problem and shown the first steps he can take to overcome it by trained counselors in a detoxification and rehabilitation center, the great majority of which are AA-oriented. A later chapter will deal with these places, which have a high degree of success in helping alcoholics recover from their illness.

Can a man or woman who is suffering from an "average" Monday-morning hangover be approached?

Yes, but not with a recital of complaints or hurt recriminations, for God's sake. That's the worst thing you can do for an alcoholic, no matter how justified you may think you are in letting him have it, pow!

What do you advise, then?

In the first place, approaching the alcoholic is not a one-time thing. Perhaps a husband or wife, friends or neighbors have sold the problem drinker on the fact that he or she needs help the first time around, but, if so, these cases must be in the vast minority. It takes time and patience to make the problem drinker see that he's not being blamed for anything; that the one making the approach understands something of what the alcoholic is going through and sympathizes with him in his ordeal; that win, lose, or draw, the spouse, the son, or daughter, the employer, neighbor, or friend is with the alcoholic all the way. Also, it sometimes takes a lot of moxie to roll under the tortured alcoholic's hurtful and even cruel rebuffs without hitting back.

You mentioned the alcoholic's employer. Is his approach different from the spouse's or the friend's?

Yes, because there's a different relationship here.

In the past, the alcoholic's employer put up with the problem drinker until he got too drunk to do his job; then the drinker was fired. Today, however, there is rapidly expanding recognition of the valuable work being done in alcoholism programs operated by big corporations and small companies alike throughout the country. Instead of the alcoholic employee being fired, he or she is offered counseling and medical treatment, if needed, and directed to Alcoholics Anonymous or occasionally to some other agency concerned with alcoholism. The corporate viewpoint has changed or is changing to consider alcoholism in an employee the same as any other grave illness. This new understanding alone has had a terrific effect on the alcoholic's viewpoint as it regards his own problem.

Still, with all this newfound understanding of the alcoholic employee's problem, the employer has an "or else" advantage that the spouse, child, or friend lack. The alcoholic employee knows what will happen to the job if he or she refuses to go along with the counseling, the hospitalization, or the AA follow-up. There may be a lot of grumbling, a side-of-the-mouth muttering that all this is a lot of unnecessary damned foolishness, but the alcoholic usually goes along.

The employer/alcoholic employee relationship will be dealt with more fully in Chapter Ten: How to Handle the Alcoholic Employee.

How about the spouse using the same "or else" technique?

At the start? No, mur*der!* Without trying to complicate things too much at this point, we'll agree that there may come a time when the spouse sees that he or she is actually hurting the alcoholic's chances for recovery by protecting, cushioning, trying to solve a problem that belongs to the alcoholic and to the alcoholic alone. Then, and only after counseling *by those qualified to view the situation objectively,* the spouse may say "or else." Then he or she must stick to it, no matter how much it hurts.

Wouldn't our family doctor be a good one to make the first approach?

If your problem drinker has had any contact at all with your doctor, chances are that Doc has already said something, if only to advise your alcoholic to try tapering off.

Increasing numbers of physicians are coming to grips with the problem of alcoholism and are involving themselves in detoxification and rehabilitation programs, urging their alcoholic patients to go to AA, helping arrange AA entree into hospitals. But the sad fact remains that our medical schools have not caught up with the rest of the world. Very few new doctors learn what alcoholism is and how it should be treated from their textbooks or their professors.

If you're fortunate enough to have an enlightened family doctor, fine. He should be of great help in making the initial approach. If you have one of the "willpower boys" or a doctor who "won't waste my valuable time on an alco-

holic"—or one who might be busy denying he has a problem himself—forget it.

How about our pastor?

More and more priests, ministers, and rabbis are learning through study and counseling training that alcoholism
is a disease with side effects that play havoc with the victim's spiritual values.

These informed men of the cloth are quick to admit
that in its relatively few years of existence, Alcoholics
Anonymous has completely eclipsed all organized religion's
efforts over the centuries in helping drunks get sober and
stay sober. They are 100 percent behind the AA program
which is one of the reasons that, although AA is not allied
with any sect, denomination, or (religious) institution, so
many AA groups hold their meetings in church buildings.

Unless your pastor is an ultrafundamentalist who still
thinks that alcoholism is a sin, he should be of great help—
after your problem drinker has admitted that he or she
can't hack it alone.

Until that day, don't—repeat, *don't*—make the mistake
of asking your pastor to "drop in" unexpectedly to talk to
Harry or Madge about his or her drinking. Even if your
pastor will go for it, chances are that the only result will
be another big, fat resentment.

*Aside from the trained counselors in those rehabilitation
centers you mentioned earlier—which, by the way, sound
too expensive and too much like committing my problem
drinker to a nuthouse . . .*

Before you go any further, there'll be more information on this subject which may change your mind about the expense, as balanced against the benefits, and which certainly should disabuse you of the idea that your problem drinker would be "committed" if entered into a rehab center.

Who should make the first approaches to the alcoholic?

Obviously, the person with the best chance of getting through to him. This is not necessarily the one he loved or respected or trusted the most before the disease robbed him of his ability to love, respect, or trust.

Because of the nature of the disease, all approaches to the alcoholic must be made with one purpose in mind—to enable the problem drinker to reach the decision to seek help *on his own.* Any attempts to force this decision—except in the employer's position—may bring a bad backlash.

So approaching the alcoholic really means patiently waiting and unobtrusively guiding the alcoholic to the point where he can approach the problem himself?

More or less. There is an old and hard-to-accept truth emphasized by recovered alcoholics that no alcoholic really does anything meaningful about his problem until he has "reached his bottom."

This is about as positive a statement as can be made about the whole mysterious, rule-shattering illness.

Does "the bottom" mean the gutter?

No, it doesn't necessarily mean Skid Row or anything like it. An alcoholic may reach his or her individual "bottom" in a luxurious penthouse, at the top desk of a big corporation, as a wife and mother still possessing her husband's and children's love and affection. Or it can be reached in a cheap motel room, in a jail cell, or in an alcoholic ward. It's the moment when the alcoholic knows that all the scrambling, all the fervent resolves to quit, all the efforts to control the disastrous drinking have failed.

It's the moment of truth, when the alcoholic admits that his or her life has become unmanageable because of the use of alcohol.

Can't I do something besides stand by and wait for my problem drinker to "hit bottom"?

Of course you can. You can prepare for that day by learning all about his or her problem, knowing that help is available when the time comes, and making sure that when the alcoholic calls for help that help comes a-runnin'.

You can contact Alcoholics Anonymous (your phone book has the number) and, through AA, Al-Anon. Both will be of immense help, not only in getting everything set for the day your problem drinker hits bottom, but just as importantly, in helping you cope with your own bad time. This should be your first move and you should not put it off.

If you live in a large city, chances are that there's a National Council on Alcoholism office in your town. This is an excellent source of information. In other places, the Mental Health Association office will have information on alcoholism. Don't let the name scare you off.

What next?

Attend two or three open AA meetings—that is, meetings where nonalcoholics are welcome. Talk over your situation with these understanding men and women. Get some phone numbers to call when your problem drinker finally agrees to accept help.

If your doctor needs to be briefed, make sure he's brought up to date so that if your alcoholic needs hospitalization, there'll be no delay in arranging for a bed.

Fix things so that when the big moment arrives, a phone call to the right people is made *within three minutes* and the alcoholic is in the proper hands *within a maximum of three hours*. Any delay could be fatal.

Anything else?

Yes. Without making a federal case out of it, you can leave literature dealing with alcoholism (furnished by your friendly AA, Al-Anon, or N.C.A.) where the alcoholic can see it—and read it more often than you might think, although on the sly. Furthermore, you can arrange casual contacts with men or women who have arrested their alcoholism. These recovered alcoholics will not try to sell a bill of goods to the suffering alcoholic unless he or she asks questions. But just seeing a onetime lush enjoying life, able to live a full, rewarding day without having to take a drink, will make a tremendous impression on the problem drinker—even though he might be the last to admit it.

Does long-distance help work? Suppose I have a sister in another city and her husband writes that she is having a bad time with booze. Will it help to send AA or other literature about alcoholism?

It can't hurt. But a more effective course would be to impress on the husband the fact that he should contact AA in his city, investigate Al-Anon, and take the other steps listed above to prepare for the day your sister calls for help.

Should we invite Joe and Susie, who have a drinking problem, to our cocktail parties? Or should we just have them over for cards and serve soft drinks?

Whether Joe and Susie drink at your party or someplace else will make no difference in the progress of their disease. So if they're still good company and won't ruin things by fighting, breaking furniture, making passes at the wrong people, or throwing up, why not include them? As for the card party with soft drinks bit, you might be able to put them through this once, but not twice.

Should the wife of an alcoholic go to social affairs by herself when he can't or won't go with her? Or should she stay home with him to prove, as you put it, that she's on his side despite everything?

The men and women in Al-Anon, AA's companion fellowship for the nonalcoholic spouses, relatives, and friends of alcoholics, stress the value of what they call "loving detachment." Too briefly, this means the nonalcoholic's refusal to let the alcoholic wreck both their lives instead of his or her own. A wretched, confused, fearful, uninformed nonalcoholic spouse is in no shape to make the right moves when the time comes.

This "loving detachment" includes occasions when the nonalcoholic will leave the alcoholic to his or her own misery while he or she goes out to live a life of his or her own. However, it does not mean desertion: The alcoholic is persistently reminded that the nonalcoholic is always standing by, awaiting the time when the problem drinker admits the problem and does something about it.

If an obstreperous alcoholic is cut off the invitation lists because of his (or her) objectionable antics, would it be helpful or otherwise for him to be told flat out why he's being excluded?

It's twenty to one he has a pretty good idea of why he wasn't invited (not that he'll admit that he shouldn't be), so a frank explanation, given in the right way, might help him finally stop kidding himself. But be warned: the immediate reaction is liable to be explosive.

Does that mean that I'll lose this friend forever?

One thing is sure: If the alcoholic doesn't stop drinking, you'll certainly lose your friend forever, the hard way. Leveling with him or her about the situation may bring a torrent of angry, reproachful, defensive, and downright abusive language, but if and when the friend recovers, all the old resentments will be thrown out with the rest of alcoholism's accumulated garbage, including the resentment against you.

How does one go about helping an alcoholic co-worker?

Not by covering up for him—at least not beyond the first couple of times.

We realize that turning in the alcoholic co-worker for his or her own good is a lot easier said than done. We all have a healthy dread of being considered a fink. Most of us would much rather put in the extra time and effort required to cover up for the irresponsible, ineffectual drunk than blow the whistle, even though we realize that our cover-up is merely postponing the inevitable.

If the co-worker can claim a friendship dating back to before the drinking got real bad, the situation can be even harder to deal with. There's the fear that it would be basely disloyal to refuse to cover up for him "until he snaps out of it." "He'd do the same for me," we say, and keep on, growing more resentful all the time. Then, when the crash comes, as likely as not we're deeply hurt to learn that the fired boozer blames us for not managing to keep the boss from ever finding out.

Unless your company has a definite "troubled employee" program, probably your best course would be to honestly warn the alcoholic co-worker that he can't expect you to aid and abet his drinking problem by covering up for him. Urge him to seek help, but don't let your sympathy or possible fear of being called a snitch make you weaken "just one more time."

Hard lines, but you might be the one who presses the drunk's button.

Is it better to try to keep a home together for the chil-
dren's sake, no matter how chaotic or even violence-torn,
than to pack up and leave, staying away until the alco-
holic responsible for the confusion decides to do some-
thing about his or her drinking?

Tough question. If the wife (or husband) and kids have
the strength and understanding available to them through
the Al-Anon and Al-Ateen programs, for instance, they
will be able to endure the usual troubles spinning off from
the alcoholic's illness. However, no child or mother—or
father, for that matter—should be expected to stand still
for drunken violence, and if the alcoholic's insanities are
visibly traumatic to the children, affecting their own mental health, perhaps they would be better off away from the
disrupted home for a while.

However, it's important that the separation be made as
a last resort and with no bitterness. The children should
be fully convinced that the drinking parent is sick, not
changed into a monster, and although there's still as much
love there as ever, it's best that he or she be left for his or
her own good.

Such decisions, of course, are not hastily arrived at and
there are so many variables in the individual situation—
usually economic—that it's impossible to offer anything
like a blanket rule covering every case.

How about "throwing the bum out"? Wouldn't that make
the alcoholic face his problem that much sooner?

"Throw the bum out!" is a phrase that rolls off the
tongue easily, but it just doesn't work in the alcoholic's

case. Even if the drunk can be evicted (presumably with the help of muscular relatives, friends, and/or neighbors) he always comes back.

The only practical separation necessitates the family ceding the house to the out-of-control alcoholic parent and staying with friends or relatives until the worst is over—or until the decision to make the separation permanent is finally reached.

Should the family move back in if the alcoholic sobers up and promises to do better, even though he or she refuses to seek help on the main problem?

Not if this is the fourth or fifth rerun of the same scene. But certainly the first time this happens, the wife (or husband) and kids should return, if only to prove to the drunk that it was the effects of the disease that were unbearable, not the alcoholic. However, if the family returns time after time, the alcoholic will start thinking it's all part of a funny game.

Well, then, what is the cutoff point, when the spouse and family refuse to return until the drunk seeks help?

To this question, a computer would reply: "Insufficient input."

It's up to those closest to the situation to decide if and when the last-resort step must be taken. Outside counseling helps, but the decision still has to be made by the spouse. And he or she must approach this step only after every other effort to help has been given a sincere try—including an honest look at the nonalcoholic's own actions and attitudes which may have contributed to the sick person's stubbornness in refusing to admit that a booze problem exists.

What do you mean, **the spouse's** *actions and attitudes?* *After all the nonalcoholic has put up with, you say the* **spouse** *is to blame?*

Whoa. We never use the word "blame" in trying to explain alcoholism and its effects, any more than we would "blame" anybody for suffering from gallstones.

However, alcoholism is a disease that affects the whole family. Unless the long-suffering spouse learns everything there is to be known about the illness, he or she (especially he) very well might unknowingly and with the best of intentions do exactly the wrong thing, which might delay or even wreck the problem drinker's chances of recovery.

That's why Al-Anon offers such a priceless opportunity to the nonalcoholic wife or husband of a drunk, especially the husband. Membership in this splendid organization, or at the very least a trial visit to an Al-Anon meeting or two (with absolutely no dues or fees required, then or ever), can't be too highly recommended.

Why do you say "especially the husband"?

Because cruel experience has proved that it is ten times as hard for a nonalcoholic husband to understand and accept his wife's alcoholism and deal with it intelligently and compassionately as it is the other way around. Blame it on the old double standard or plain male chauvinism, but the nonalcoholic man has much more trouble believing his wife really is suffering from a disease than the nonalcoholic wife does in regard to her husband. Husbands just can't seem to get it through their heads that the alcoholic wife did or said certain things while in a blackout, for instance. The feeling persists that the husband, as the "head of the family," the "guy that gives the orders," missed out somewhere along the line when he didn't make his wife stop drinking too much.

Then, too, let's face it, the husband is often reluctant to go to and stay with Al-Anon, where he could have all his misconceptions cleared up, because, as of now, the Al-Anon membership is predominantly female, although it is constantly changing toward a more nearly equal male–female ratio. He may feel that to take advice from a group of women might, God help him, cast reflections on his masculinity.

It has been further proved that even when the alcoholic wife finds sobriety in AA, the nonalcoholic husband is far less cooperative in helping her work her program than the nonalcoholic wife is in helping her husband. Too many husbands seem to feel that once the wife has stopped drinking, that's it, and are too often anxious to get back to the social life they had before the wife's drinking got bad.

As hard as it is to say, it's true: The fully informed and fully cooperative nonalcoholic husband of an alcoholic wife is the exception to the rule.

Okay, okay, I love my alcoholic wife too much to fail her, no matter how she drives me up the wall. What's my starting point toward helping her?

A good place to start is with yourself. Remember, you're emotionally involved in this situation and chances are you're not thinking straight where she's concerned. When you get as many facts concerning the disease as you can, see how these facts apply to your attitudes and reactions. There are going to be a lot of readjustments to be made, so start with your own, *not* the alcoholic's.

When the drunk seems to deliberately goad me into losing my temper, can I be blamed for popping off at her (or him) occasionally?

Blowing your stack may make you think you feel better at the time, but deep down you know you don't—not really. By cussing her out, scolding, blaming, hurling recriminations (or left hooks), and moralizing, you're tearing yourself up at the same time you're doing no more for the alcoholic than adding to a burden of guilt, the weight of which is impossible for a nonalcoholic to realize.

We know the advice—*Don't lose your temper*—is a lot easier to give than to follow, but it's important. Remember, you can always walk away. To become embroiled in a verbal or real slugfest is to play into the hands of the enemy, alcoholism.

Does it do any good to search out all those hidden bottles and pour the booze down the drain?

Not a bit. The alcoholic can always find more to drink. Pouring liquor down the drain is expensive, humiliating, and useless.

You've already advised against covering up for an alcoholic co-worker, but how about a wife protecting a drunk husband where there's a job at stake or bad checks floating around or bill collectors knocking at the door?

Here again, the advice is easy to give, hard to take, and imperative.

Don't do anything to delay the crisis that may save the alcoholic's life. By cushioning the blows dealt by the problem drinker's irresponsibility, you're only postponing the inevitable. The crash that will come after you stop futilely trying to ward it off may very well make the problem drinker admit he's in bad trouble and seek help.

Covering up with lies to the boss or by pleading with him to give Joe another chance, making good the bad checks, scraping up the money to meet the bills, or hiding the car keys so he won't get picked up on a drunk driving charge are the natural inclinations of a loving wife, but they're wrong, dead wrong. And we use the word "dead" advisedly.

The same advice applies to the husband who feels it's his duty to lie for his alcoholic wife to save her from embarrassment or to keep others from finding out she has a drinking problem. The opposite is true: It's his duty to bring her eyeball-to-eyeball with the fact that she's in trouble as soon as possible, so that she may not have to travel the whole route.

"Saving" the alcoholic from the ruinous results of his or her drinking keeps the problem drinker from reaching the "bottom" that has to be hit before the alcoholic admits he or she can't handle it alone. That's the reason so few extremely wealthy acoholics ever recover.

Have you any more Don'ts that might be a little easier to follow?

The best place to get the real scoop from others who have gone through what you're going through is an open AA meeting or an Al-Anon meeting, but for now, here's one we can't resist:

Don't give the suffering alcoholic the line: "If you loved me, you'd control your drinking." You might as well tell a diabetic: "If you loved me, you could eat sweets."

Almost without exception, the alcoholic's love for his or her spouse has nothing whatever to do with either the contraction of the disease or its progress.

How about dropping admiring remarks about a recovered alcoholic we both know?

That's as surefire a way as any to turn your alcoholic off. And don't worry: your problem drinker already admires and envies any recovered alcoholic he or she may know. Undoubtedly, he thinks his case is "different," but the proof of the possibility of recovery is always there, and, hopefully, when the time comes, he'll realize that what worked for one alcoholic can work for him—that is, if you haven't made him despise all thought of the recovery program by continually pointing at the recovered alcoholic as a shining example.

One or two mentions of the fact that So-and-so certainly

looks and acts great since he or she stopped drinking is enough. To belabor the point is to defeat the purpose.

How about being extra nice to the problem drinker when he goes on the wagon or cuts down on his drinking?

If being "extra nice" means what we think it means, we feel that that's misusing something precious, offering it as a reward or withholding it as a penalty. Rewards and promises, along with coaxing, arguments, and threats, can all be placed in the same category when dealing with alcoholism: none of them works, or at least not for long.

Is there any last all-important Do or Don't?

Yes, don't just sit there—do something!

Most of us would rather let a difficult situation slide along than take action. We hope that something will turn up to make the trouble go away. With alcoholism, nothing is going to turn up. The trouble is not going to go away by itself. The victim will get steadily worse, the situation will steadily deteriorate, *unless* you start right *now* to learn all you can about alcoholism, understand the part you can intelligently play in helping the alcoholic, and lay plans for the time when the problem drinker finally asks for help.

Just sitting there wishing is not only futile, it's almost criminal.

Sources of Effective Help

From what I've read so far, I can assume that now, when you start dealing with the help that's available to my problem drinker (and to me, too, I hope), you're going to bear down hard on Alcoholics Anonymous, right?

Right, although other avenues of help for the alcoholic will be explored.

Does that mean that you speak for AA, that this is an official AA publication?

An emphatic no to both questions. This book is an offering of the New Life Foundation. The New Life Foundation has no connection, official or otherwise, with Alcoholics Anonymous, As mentioned earlier, information volunteered by members of AA, along with that supplied by nonalcoholics who are especially informed on the subject of alcoholism, has gone into the compilation of this book.

This book certainly has an AA-directed thrust because our conviction agrees with that of virtually every other qualified spokesman on the subject of alcoholism—that, in other words, in its relatively few years of existence, AA has done more to give the alcoholic a rewarding life of anxiety-free sobriety than all other agencies combined, back to the beginning of recorded history.

Many authorities not given to reckless statements say that AA is the *only* hope for the suffering alcoholic. While we maintain it is the most rewarding, most successful course of action toward recovery yet discovered, we would be less than objective if we didn't agree that alcoholics have found sobriety by means other than AA.

What's the recovery percentage claimed by AA?

Right away we get into percentages, eh?

Not to duck the question, but we must warn you at the start that AA has been called "the most disorganized organization in the world." It has no corporate structure, no chiefs, only Indians. It is a highly individualistic program with the thousands of local groups that make up AA wielding complete autonomy. Above all, it has no statisticians, no computer bank to supply a readout on how many men and women found a new way of life in AA or what percentage of those who tried it didn't make it. There are no attendance records kept and what membership rolls there are are extremely loose. Therefore, any statistics offered must necessarily be very iffy.

However, if you insist on some figures, we can offer the results of a widespread (although strictly anonymous) survey conducted a few years ago for the General Service Board of AA. That survey showed that 62.5 percent of the men and 67.5 percent of the women included in the survey stopped drinking within a year after joining AA, giving a mean average of 65 percent.*

It has been more loosely estimated that of all the hundreds of thousands who have given AA a fair trial (say, at least ninety days), more than 60 percent have latched on with no serious trouble thereafter. Of the 40 percent who didn't make it on the first go-round, it has been estimated that at least 40 percent went back to AA and found sobriety on the second, third, or even the twentieth try.

Put up against 2-percent, 4-percent, or even 8-percent recovery ratios claimed in other quarters, these figures are truly impressive.

If there are no chiefs, only Indians, and nobody to give the orders, how does AA keep going?

As the bumblebee should not be able to fly, according to all aeronautical engineering standards, so should AA not be able to not only keep going but to keep growing. But it does—probably because there *are* no orders given in AA, by anyone, to anyone.

How many people are in AA?

More statistics? As of this writing, a *rough* guess would be 600,000 in the U.S. alone. By the time you read this, the number of recovering alcoholics in AA undoubtedly will be higher.

* Peter Bourne and Ruth Fox, eds., *Alcoholism: Progress in Research & Treatment* (New York: Academic Press, 1973).

Do you mean that AA exists in other countries?

Yes, there are AA groups in nearly every country on the face of the globe, except those behind the Iron Curtain. One of the strengths of the program is that no matter where an AA goes, he or she is never out of reach of friends in AA. Some more well-to-do AAs go on world cruises with the main purpose of visiting AA groups in foreign countries.

Do you mean there's a lighthearted side to AA?

Absolutely. In spite of the reason for its being, Alcoholics Anonymous is basically a *happy* program. Outsiders and newcomers to the AA program are continually amazed at discovering that there's a lot of fun attached to AA.

Do you mean that these alcoholics, with all the misery they've suffered and caused, can find happiness just by joining AA?

There's a lot more to it than that, but happy sobriety is the end product. If that's hard to believe, just attend an open AA meeting and look at the faces, listen to the laughter.

What does my problem drinker have to do to join AA?

The only requirement for membership is a desire to stop drinking—the alcoholic's desire—not his wife's, not her husband's, not the parents' or the family's or the friends'.

What does it cost?

One more time: not a nickel. AA is supported entirely by the members' dimes, quarters, and dollar bills that are dropped in the basket when it's passed around at the end of a meeting. If somebody is suffering from an acute case of the tights, he feels perfectly free to bypass the passed basket till things get better. Nobody knows or gives a damn about how much the man or woman next to him contributes. This is one organization in which one's money or lack of it is of absolutely no importance.

Unique in this day and age, isn't it?

In any day and age. In the early days of AA cynics and skeptics spent a lot of time and effort trying to find a gimmick. It was impossible for them to accept a bunch of ex-drunks doing what they did for the still suffering alcoholics without some kind of a payoff.

What they failed to understand (and what a lot of people still fail to grasp) is that most of these ex-drunks must depend on their work with other alcoholics, freely and joyously given, to help keep them sober. That, to them, is the biggest payoff of all.

Okay, so my problem drinker finally makes the decision to seek help from AA. How does he go about it and what can he expect?

When the call is made to the AA number listed in the telephone directory, it will bring an early visit by one or two AAs. Ordinarily, men answer a call made for a man, women call on a woman. This is known in AA parlance as a "Twelfth Step call," deriving from that part of the Twelfth Step of the AA philosophy which states: ". . . . we tried to carry this message to alcoholics. . . ."

There is no hard sell connected with this call. The suffering alcoholic is simply assured that if he or she has had enough, there are uncounted numbers of new friends standing by who want to help with the problem. The alcoholic learns that his visitors have been as bad off, or worse, than he is at the moment, as hard as that may be for him to believe. These visitors listen to the alcoholic with full understanding and without a trace of censure or superiority, because they've been there themselves.

The Twelfth Step callers explain something of what AA is all about—not a great deal, because the alcoholic is seldom in any condition to grasp or retain much. The important thing is that they impress on the sick person the fact that he or she doesn't have to scramble any longer, that all the help he or she needs to get well is right there, ready to go to work. Then, as soon as the alcoholic is physically able, he or she is taken or directed to a meeting.

That's all there is to it?

No, of course not. The above explanation has been oversimplified. Every Twelfth Step call is different. The callers play it by ear, drawing on their own experience and what they've learned from others. The alcoholic might need hospitalization or other medical attention which the Twelfth Steppers might assist in arranging. He or she might need somebody to stay on to help the sick person to sweat it out without reaching for the jug. But be assured that if the alcoholic really wants to stop drinking, AA will go to almost any lengths to help him or her get sober and stay that way.

What if the alcoholic changes his mind after the phone call is made and turns off the Twelfth Step callers when they ring the doorbell? Does that put him on the AA blacklist?

There's no such thing as an AA blacklist. There have been drunks who have tried to play unbelievably outrageous games with AA and the worst that has been said of them was: "Some of us are sicker than others."

If the person calling AA has second thoughts about needing help—or flat out loses his nerve—the Twelfth Steppers wish the drunk well, possibly leave some literature, and bow out with the sincere reminder that if AA is called again, they or somebody like them will be more than glad to come back.

The door to AA is always left open, never slammed shut.

What is an AA meeting like?

There are two general types of meetings—the open meeting and the closed meeting.

The open meeting is one at which nonalcoholics are welcome. They usually are speakers' meetings at which two AAs tell what it was like with them before AA, how they found AA, and what it has been like since. The talks are usually followed by a social get-together over coffee, and it's a good time for the concerned nonalcoholic to get a firsthand look at the type of people in AA, collect some phone numbers to call when the suffering alcoholic finally decides that he or she has had enough, and to pick up some helpful literature, of which there's a plentiful and free supply.

The closed meeting is attended only by alcoholics. It is usually a discussion meeting at which any AA who has an alcohol-related problem that's been troublesome can throw it out to be kicked around by the others in search of an answer.

One rather singular fact should be mentioned here: Direct advice is almost never given in AA. Instead, members who have had a similar problem tell how they dealt with it, or they might explain the way the roadblock was handled by somebody else in their experience.

If there are no pressing problems to be talked over, the chairman of the closed meeting offers a subject for discussion. The AAs around the table are free to digress from this subect so long as the digression concerns the alcoholic problem.

Open meetings usually run for an hour. Discussion meetings are generally scheduled for an hour and a half, but the time limit, as with everything else in AA, is very elastic.

If a person goes to AA and keeps on drinking, do they throw him out?

Only if he's so drunk that he disrupts the meeting. And even then, he's not thrown out; he's quietly, compassionately, asked to leave and come back when he's sober enough to listen with some degree of understanding.

It happens—although not too often—that a man or woman will keep nipping and going to AA for days and weeks and months, playing a funny game, thinking that nobody could possibly guess. This goes on until one of two things happens; either it dawns on the game player that he's kidding nobody but himself, or he gets falling-down drunk. In either case, the nipper inevitably finds out that his fellow AAs knew what he was doing all along.

You see, it's almost impossible to con AA. The fellowship is made up of men and women who were con artists themselves in their drinking days and who can still spot a phony at two miles in a heavy fog.

What turns all these con artists and other types of anti-social misfits into a crowd of do-gooders? Do they all "get religion"?

First, AA is not a crowd of do-gooders in the accepted and slightly jeering sense of the word. Secondly, they do not "get religion" if that term is meant to imply that Alcoholics Anonymous is a religious organization. It is not. The AA program which so many recovered alcoholics are following has a strong spiritual foundation, but each member develops his spiritual values according to his or her needs along the lines most acceptable to the individual member. AA believes that success in the program depends heavily on the recovering alcoholic's recognition of his need for help from a higher power. However, nobody dictates what form that higher power must take in the mind of the individual.

Many AAs regard their individual group or the fellowship as a whole as their higher power.

But if AAs go to any lengths to help a suffering alcoholic, as you say they do, freely giving of their time and effort with no expectation of reward, why aren't they do-gooders?

AAs believe they are rewarded, in full measure, heaped up and overflowing, for all they do when they try to help other alcoholics. Most of them believe that their own sobriety could not endure long—and certainly would lose its happy quality—if they didn't keep on with this work.

Members of AA continually refer to it as a "selfish program," much to the bewilderment and even annoyance of non-AAs. The above might explain one of the reasons they say this.

I've heard Alcoholics Anonymous called group therapy that has been hoked up with a lot of mystery. Care to comment?

Various forms of group therapy have been tried in the fight against alcoholism ever since the idea first emerged in psychiatric and psychological circles. Its success in achieving long-term sobriety for the alcoholic has been very limited, as measured against the proven value of group therapy in areas other than alcoholism.

As far as AA being hoked up with a lot of mystery, that's just not true. Every last part of the program has been explained in detail a hundred times over in official AA publications. Far from striving for an air of hokey mystery, one of the main tenets of AA is: *Keep it simple!*

Well, then, why all the hush-hush anonymity?

There are several vital reasons for that second "A" in AA.

First, there's many a sick alcoholic who would shy away from his last chance to live if, in his mixed-up mind, he thought everybody would know of his "disgrace" in having to turn to AA. Later, when he looks back on it, that same recovered alcoholic probably will laugh at his fears, but they are very real to him at the crucial time. The sincere pledge that his or her anonymity will be protected in AA has often meant the life-or-death difference in an alcoholic's decision.

Secondly, and perhaps more importantly, by maintaining anonymity—strictly at the public level and to a certain degree within the fellowship, too—the possibility of status-seeking troubles is reduced to a bare minimum, if not totally eliminated. One of AA's great blessings is the anonymity of service. One alcoholic helps another without either knowing or caring how much money one has, what the other's background might be, what titles, jail terms, Rolls Royces, or divorces either recovered alcoholic may lay claim to.

A third reason for anonymity concerns members of AA who hold positions of public trust—doctors, lawyers, bankers, elected officials, clergymen, and such. Until the last traces of stigma and suspicion are finally scrubbed from the alcoholic picture, AAs in this category pull their duty better under the protection of their anonymity.

Are there more women than men in AA?

As one male chauvinist pig once said: "No, but sometimes it sounds as though there were."

Seriously, the male–female ratio in Alcoholics Anonymous runs about five to three. There are many "men only" and "women only" groups in the larger cities, but these are invariably made up of men and women who also attend regular mixed meetings on other nights of the week.

Is there any way you can describe Alcoholics Anonymous without going into the details of the program?

It can be best described by using AA's own description of itself:

> Alcoholics Anonymous is a fellowship of men and women who share their experience, strength and hope with each other that they may solve their common problem and help others to recover from alcoholism.
>
> The only requirement for membership is a desire to stop drinking. There are no dues or fees for A.A. membership; we are self-supporting through our own contributions.
>
> A.A. is not allied with any sect, denomination, politics, organization or institution; does not wish to engage in any controversy; neither endorses nor opposes any causes.
>
> Our primary purpose is to stay sober and help other alcoholics to achieve sobriety.*

You mentioned the Twelfth Step of the AA program. How many steps are there and what do they mean?

There are twelve steps which are suggested (not dictated) as the AA way to good, solid, lasting sobriety, free of anxiety. It is not our intention to go into these steps in any detail. Their study and practice is a big part of the life that will open to your problem drinker when he or she goes to AA. They must be *lived,* not read about in a book.

However, the all-important First Step may be set down

---

* "Reprinted with permission from the A.A. Grapevine, Incorporated."

here: *"We admitted we were powerless over alcohol and that our lives had become unmanageable."* (Italics ours.)

Until and unless the problem drinker takes this First Step, the other eleven will have no real meaning for him or her.

Does AA operate any medical services?

No. Practically all federal, state, and local detoxification and rehabilitation services, as well as privately operated rehabilitation centers, are AA-*oriented*, but Alcoholics Anonymous has no official connection with them.

What can be done for a problem drinker who may admit that he needs help but who flatly refuses to have anything to do with AA? Is he or she doomed?

Of course not. The National Council on Alcoholism maintains information centers in nearly every city of any size. These offices are exactly that, places where light-shedding information about alcoholism is freely distributed. The alcoholic may inquire at an N.C.A. information center and be given just as much enlightenment as is asked for without making a commitment of any kind.

Your local Mental Health Association office in all probability offers an alcoholism program with available counseling.

Most states have alcoholic rehabilitation programs, many of which include detoxification treatment for the very sick, as well as out-patient group therapy sessions led by men and women trained in alcoholic counseling. However, in most if not all of the state-operated rehabilitation centers, your anti-AA problem drinker is going to find that at least one AA meeting a week is part of his treatment.

The same holds true for privately operated rehabilitation centers and all but the rankest "drying-out joint" type of hospitals, sanitariums, and "rest homes." They all expose their patients to AA in one way or another.

Do any nonalcoholics belong to Alcoholics Anonymous?

AA makes no attempt to label anyone alcoholic or nonalcoholic. The decision is left entirely up to the individual. Doubtless there are a few persons in the fellowship who are not alcoholics by strict definition, but they obviously feel a need for the AA program. These "pseudoalcoholics" (if there is such a term) are welcome so long as they don't try to divert the focus of the group's procedures away from AA's primary purpose—help for the alcoholic.

AA is not a sensitivity group, a kaffeeklatsch, a dating game, a sewing circle, or a Greek letter fraternity. Over the years, it has naturally attracted a scattering of "joiners," the curious, those looking for a handout, some who expect to find "a safe way to drink socially," salesmen hopeful of new business contacts, wolves on the prowl, and female barracudas on the hunt for a man. How could it help but include some of these characters, considering the hundreds of thousands who have come through the door? But the plain and simple *honesty* of the AA program has inevitably sent these jokers on their way.

Speaking of looking for a handout: If an alcoholic comes to AA in deep financial trouble, will AA give him something to tide him over?

Add to those things which AA is not: a small loan agency.

The alcoholic problem is the only problem with which AA can help the newcomer deal at the start. The alcoholic must stop drinking before anything else. His life depends on it.

The pile of debts, the outstanding bum checks, the threatened divorce, the jeopardized job may loom as problems that the poor guy is sure will destroy him unless something is done about them right now. But before anything else, he has to do something about the problem that spawned all the others—booze. AA can and will help him do this. When the newcomer is sober and working the AA program, the ways in which he can deal with all the other problems are made clear to him, and, almost without exception, these ways prove to be a lot easier than he ever dared hope.

But so far as tiding him over at the start is concerned, experience has proved that far from being a help, these handouts are a hindrance, sometimes fatal.

I've heard somewhere that an AA is allowed three slips (returns to drinking) before he's called on the carpet and warned to shape up or ship out. True?

False. There is no "carpet" or anyone in the whole vast fellowship who would even think of claiming the right to tell another AA to shape up, much less ship out. In fact, the only person who can make mention of a slip is the person who did the slipping, and always voluntarily, to square things with himself, not with anybody else.

If the slip-and-slider asks, he or she will be given friendly counsel aimed only at trying to find out why the slip happened and what safeguards might prevent a repeat performance. There's an overall understanding in AA that some people make the program more easily than others, for reasons almost as mysterious as the disease itself.

Or perhaps we should take back that last statement. In most thoughtful opinions, the ease of success in AA can be generally predicated on the individual's degree of acceptance of and commitment to the AA program.

You've mentioned Al-Anon frequently. Can you be a little more specific about its makeup, function, and requirements?

Very briefly, Al-Anon offers a program of help for the nonalcoholic spouse, relative, or friend of the alcoholic, which is patterned closely after the program of Alcoholics Anonymous.

The same stress on anonymity prevails. Al-Anon has Twelve Steps which are very similar to the Twelve Steps of AA, including the First Step in which the nonalcoholic admits that he or she is powerless over alcohol but as it affects the alcoholic with whom he or she is concerned, not the Al-Anon.

In Al-Anon the nonalcoholic learns the facts about the nature of the disease and what he or she can do to help the alcoholic find sobriety and maintain it once it is found. Perhaps more important, the nonalcoholic is led to examine himself or herself honestly and to deal intelligently with the fears, doubts, resentments, and other hangups that the Al-Anon may be suffering because of the spouse's, relative's, or friend's alcoholism.

As in AA, there are no dues or fees. Meetings are usually, but not always, held in conjunction with AA meetings, but in a separate room. These are usually discussion meetings but occasionally there are speakers—sometimes a guest speaker from AA. Once in a while, joint AA–Al-Anon meetings are held.

An important part of the Al-Anon program is the telephone communication between members. Phone numbers are freely exchanged (usually on a first-name-only basis), and whenever a sticky problem arises that can't wait for the next meeting, the Al-Anon gets on the horn to talk it over with other members, seeking advice, encouragement, or just a chat with an understanding friend.

Although they are closely parallel organizations with a common objective—dealing with the alcoholism problem— AA and Al-Anon are separate entities. There is one major difference between the two: AA is made up entirely of recovered alcoholics and alcoholics who are working to find sobriety; Al-Anon includes in its membership those whose husbands, wives, relatives, or friends are in AA as well as those whose individual problem drinkers are still lapping up the booze.

In other words, the wife of an alcoholic husband (or vice versa) can join Al-Anon even if the spouse is not in AA?

Certainly. As in AA, statistics are pretty shaky in Al-Anon, but it's safe to say that at least half the men and women coming into Al-Anon did so before their wives or husbands (or relatives or friends) found AA.

Also, it's sad but true that some of those alcoholics never have stopped drinking. Still, the Al-Anon program has proved an invaluable source of strength for the nonalcoholic in keeping his or her own life—and the family's— from going down the drain along with the drunk's.

If my problem drinker joins AA, what's to be gained by my joining Al-Anon? Isn't his (or her) sobriety enough?

Let's put it this way: If the only thing your joining Al-Anon accomplished would be to help your problem drinker latch on to the AA program and make steady progress, wouldn't that make it worthwhile?

Actually, while Al-Anon membership is very valuable to the spouse who is in AA, it is even more valuable to the nonalcoholic. Time after time the statement is made: "I came to Al-Anon to find out what I could do for my wife (or husband) and found to my amazement that the main thing was what I could do for myself."

We suggest that you go to one Al-Anon meeting, listen, ask some questions, and pick up some literature. If nothing else, this visit will disabuse you of the possible misconception that an Al-Anon meeting is a gathering of bitchy wives and sour husbands who sit around and gripe about how badly they've been treated by their alcoholic mates. It's anything but that, take our word for it.

If Al-Anon doesn't have a separate listing in your telephone directory, call the AA number and ask where and when the next Al-Anon meeting will be held. Then go.

You're assured of a warm welcome, and a nicer bunch of people you'll never meet. And, as life insurance ads would put it, it's strictly a no-obligation deal.

How come you can make such an all-out, unabashed plug for Al-Anon when you haven't been half so hard sell about Alcoholics Anonymous?

The achievements, purposes, and philosophy of AA can never be overestimated. It has been seriously stated that when historians list man's major accomplishments of the twentieth century, the birth and growth of Alcoholics Anonymous will be at, or very close to, the top. The gratitude of millions of men and women—yes, and youngsters, too—whose lives would have been a shambles if it had not been for AA gives testimony to the validity of this statement.

However, AA is and always has been "a program of attraction, not promotion." An alcoholic's decision to go to AA must be his or her own for the program to do much good. Sincerely enthusiastic endorsements are fine, and greatly deserved, but even the highest-minded arguments should not be used to force the alcoholic to go to AA against his or her will. It simply will not work.

Al-Anon is another thing. No all-important decision must be made by the nonalcoholic who gives Al-Anon a look. Many men and women who are deeply grateful now for what the Al-Anon program has done for them attended their first meeting much against their will. Some were suspicious, even antagonistic to the whole idea. What they saw and heard surprised them and pleased them and made them come back. So it may be with you if you're a non-alcoholic with a spouse, relative, or close friend who has a drinking problem.

Surely it's worth an hour or so of your time to find out.

What is Al-Ateen?

Al-Ateen is a nationwide organization comprised of the children of alcoholics. In its relatively few years of existence, Al-Ateen has done great things in the field of educating these youngsters about the disease of alcoholism and in giving these impressionable kids the assurances they so desperately need.

The lives of most, if not all, children of an alcoholic parent have been blighted by shame, hate, fear, and confusion. Unless they are taught differently, most of them feel unloved, deprived, guilty, and even worthless. In Al-Ateen they learn that the alcoholic parent is sick and should not be blamed for the actions and words that have hurt them so. With understanding, almost invariably there comes a return of the child's love and compassion for the alcoholic parent. By talking with other youngsters in the same situation, the young person can straighten out the personality kinks that the drunk has created.

Al-Ateen is under the general guidance of Al-Anon, but the kids run their own show, hold their own meetings, discuss their own problems, with a bare minimum of adult supervision. A superstrict anonymity is preserved to protect the Al-Ateen from all possible hurt that might be carelessly inflicted by thoughtless and uninformed schoolmates.

The ability of the young people in Al-Ateen to grasp the alcoholism problem and to deal with it at their own level is a source of constant amazement among the AAs and Al-Anons who are privileged to see them in action.

CHAPTER

EIGHT

Detoxification and Rehabilitation

Now you're going to tell me just what kind of medical treatment or psychiatric attention my problem drinker needs, what kinds of medicine should be prescribed, where the best rehabilitation center near our home is, what they do there, how long the course of treatment will be, how much it will cost, and how much good it will do. Right?

Wrong.

While the New Life Foundation hopes through this book to answer most of the questions and clear up all the funny ideas about alcoholism, it has no intention of attempting to encroach on the areas of medicine, psychotherapy, or other professional fields. We certainly don't intend to offer any advice concerning therapy. That lies in the province of the doctor attending the alcoholic, each case being treated to meet the individual patient's needs.

What we intend to do in this chapter is present a general

115

picture, understandable to the layman, of what detoxification and alcoholic rehabilitation is all about, put to rest some misconceptions that date back to the days of the old Keeley Cure, say a word about some of the new drugs that your alcoholic may (but not necessarily will) be given during detoxification, and furnish a once-over-lightly description of what a patient might expect when he or she enters a rehabilitation center.

First of all, what's the difference between detoxification and rehabilitation?

Detoxification is the medical treatment given an alcoholic during the withdrawal period, immediately after the patient stops drinking. It's aimed at preventing alcoholic convulsions and delirium tremens and at minimizing the nervousness, nausea, insomnia, and other ailments that afflict the person who shuts off the alcoholic intake after an extended period of uncontrolled drinking.

Rehabilitation is the long-term treatment intended to interest the alcoholic in and prepare him or her for a life without booze.

Detoxification programs are usually administered in hospitals, although they can be carried out at home in less serious cases. The detoxification process usually takes from three to five days of more or less intensive hospital care—longer if the patient needs it. Rehabilitation programs are seldom less than twenty-one days in duration.

Do all hospitals admit alcoholics for detoxification?

Regrettably, as of this writing, there are more than a few hospitals that still refuse to admit patients under a diagnosis of acute alcoholism. Usually these same hospitals will take an alcoholic under another diagnosis, such as "nervous exhaustion" or some other prettier name. You would do well to check with your doctor to make sure a hospital with a detoxification program is within reach when your problem drinker needs it.

Here's an interesting aside: For years hospitals turned away alcoholics, except for emergency room treatment, out of the fear that they would be disruptive, if not dangerous, to other patients. Those who were admitted were secluded from other patients in locked wards. Fairly recently, hospital administrators and staffs have found that the alcoholic patient, admitted on the same basis as any other sick person, are the "best patients in the building" in terms of behavior. Only those in convulsions or in delirium tremens need separation from other patients.

Does an alcoholic have to have convulsions or d.t.'s to qualify for detoxification?

Good God, no! The main purpose of detoxification treatment is to get the patient better and prevent the d.t.'s or the "rum fits."

I've heard it said that it takes sixty to ninety days just to get the alcohol out of a heavy drinker's blood. Correct?

Let's emphasize here that merely ridding the blood of alcohol is the least part of the detoxification process. It's dealing with the effects of withdrawal that requires the doctors' and nurses' attention.

As to your question, the time varies but usually up to twenty-four hours is enough for this marvelous mechanism we call the human body to metabolize the alcohol in the blood.

Can you briefly tell me what the alcoholic can expect when he or she goes into a hospital for detoxification?

First of all, the alcoholic can bank on being accepted by the doctors and nurses as a physically sick person, not a screwball, a moral weakling, or a social outcast. He or she probably won't be aware of much of what is going on during the first few hours or even the first day or so, but the treatment will concentrate on correcting nutritional deficiencies, administering medication to alleviate the jitters, controlling dangerously high or low blood pressure, checking for other physical ailments that might have been masked by the patient's intoxication, looking for symptoms of possible delirium tremens which usually strike some time after the booze is shut off, and otherwise making the patient as comfortable as possible.

What is this paraldehyde that I've heard about?

You've heard so much about it because it's been around a long time. It is an effective alcohol substitute given patients undergoing withdrawal. About all we can tell you about it is that once smelled, it will never be forgotten.

In recent years, many new and effective tranquilizers

have been developed and these have replaced the use of paraldehyde in many hospitals.

Do all alcoholics need detoxification?

Let's put it this way: Anyone who stops drinking goes through the detoxification process, either under medical treatment or quitting cold turkey. As booze *in*toxicates the drinker, shutting off the alcoholic intake results in *detoxi*-fication of the abstainer.

If the drinker reaches the decision to quit while he or she is in fairly good physical shape, the detoxification process may be sweated out without calling a doctor or going to a hospital. It's a miserable experience, at best, and there's the danger that the suddenly shut-off acoholic who forgoes medical attention will go into convulsions, prolonged hallucinations, or even delirium tremens.

However, to be absolutely objective, it must be added that there are still some recovered alcoholics who will argue that the drunk who goes through this withdrawal torment the hard way and has good reason to "remember his last drunk" is less prone to go back to booze than is the person whose detoxification has been eased by medical care.

What's the majority opinion on this?

It is that the advances in medical detoxification treatment plus the enlightened attitude of hospitals in the admittance and care of alcoholics should be taken advantage of in any case in which there is the least doubt of the sufferer's ability to make it alone. Too many alcoholics have had their resolve to stop drinking first weakened and finally shattered by the severity of withdrawal discomfort.

Some of these have sought relief in the bottle for what proved to be the last time.

But isn't this, in fact, "cushioning" the drunk, as you've warned against?

Not at all. There's a big difference between treating an alcoholic under a phony diagnosis such as "executive tension" (drying him out and sending him forth with the admonition to cut down on his drinking) and detoxification treatment under the diagnosis of acute alcoholism, with the emphasis laid on the fact that as a diagnosed alcoholic the patient can never safely take another drink.

Doctors and nurses in detoxification units aren't harsh or unsympathetic but they don't fool around with the facts. They tell it like it is.

Does Alcoholics Anonymous play any part in detoxification treatment?

Not as big a part as it plays in rehabilitation, but many AAs make it a practice to call on patients under detoxification, when the patients are able to know what's going on and have evidenced an interest in AA. Most doctors urge or even insist on their alcoholic patients making contact with AA during the latter stages of detoxification. In some hospitals, regular AA meetings are held for the benefit of those detoxified patients who care to (or are told by their doctors to) attend. Again, there's no hard sell. Mainly, the patients are extended an invitation to explore AA when they leave the hospital.

Does Alcoholics Anonymous itself offer any detoxification or rehabilitation services?

No, AA is officially connected with no medical, psychotherapy, counseling, or referral service. Members of AA can and will help you obtain such services for your problem drinker, but on an individual or group basis, not as official representatives of AA. This may seem a fine line at first glance, but it's an important one to AA, which guards relentlessly against any hint of commercialism.

When is the best time to approach the alcoholic about entering a hospital for detoxification?

Ideally, when the alcoholic makes the decision to stop drinking. However, to be strictly factual, most of them are poured into the hospital when they're too sick to make a decision about anything. Some of the most successful recovered alcoholics we know admit that they came to in the hospital without the least idea of how they got there.

If the drunk is obviously in need of immediate medical attention but still able to put up an argument, promise him or her anything, but get the alcoholic to the hospital. Your conscience needn't bother you: It's a hundred to one that the drunk won't remember the promise, and, even if he does, he'll forgive you for telling a little white lie in order to save his life.

What are the mechanics of getting my alcoholic admitted to a hospital?

You should have made preparations with your doctor for speedy admittance to the hospital long before the crisis. However, if you've put it off, call an ambulance to take him or her to the emergency room. In cases of a physically violent alcoholic, call the police.

We intend to emphasize it over and over again: *intelligent preparation is of the utmost importance!* In about nine out of ten cases, this preparation has been skimped and the resultant confusion and delay have been disastrous.

Can't the alcoholic get hooked as badly on the sedatives given in detoxification treatment as he or she was hooked on liquor?

Lamentably, the answer is yes.

Tranquilizers used in detoxification are of immense value when their use is carefully controlled by physician and nurse. When the alcoholic leaves the hospital, however, he's often more or less on his own as regards the number of pills he takes and for how long he keeps on with them. It must be impressed on him (or her) that pill addiction is a very dangerous possibility and that a person who is "on pills" is as bad off if not worse off than the uncontrolled drinker.

The sooner the detoxified alcoholic shuts off the tranquilizers entirely, the better.

Is Antabuse one of the tranquilizers given in detoxification?

No, Antabuse (generic name: disulfiram) is known as a deterrent drug or an "alcohol-antagonizing" drug. Anyone who ingests an Antabuse tablet cannot drink alcohol *in any form or strength* for at least seventy-two hours without suffering violent discomfort, including extreme nausea, vomiting, palpitations, labored breathing, and blurred vision.

The purpose of Antabuse is to make it physically impossible for the newly dried-out alcoholic to take a drink. It is a prescription drug and should not be administered to a patient without a prior physical examination. It should *never* be slipped over on a person who's drinking to—God forbid—"teach him a lesson." Under certain conditions it could be a disastrous and even a deadly trick.

Usually, the alcoholic who is put on Antabuse is given a carefully controlled sample of what will happen to him if he takes a drink on top of the pill. This is usually enough to instill a fear of the consequences which will endure until the recovered alcoholic's thinking begins to straighten out and he feels he can make it without Antabuse.

Antabuse is not generally intended as a long-term treatment, although we know of several recovered alcoholics who augment their AA or other recovery program with regular or occasional doses of Antabuse. It helps the newly sober person who finds himself or herself incontrovertibly committed to a situation where there is a lot of drinking going on to know that he or she has taken a pill which forces a "No thanks" to the most insidious invitation to join the folks at the bar.

Those who support the Antabuse treatment argue that under it the newly recovered alcoholic has to make only one decision each day, to swallow a pill that's a little bigger than an aspirin. For the rest of that day, he or she can walk past bars and package stores, turn down invitations to have a short one, and otherwise stay away from alcohol in the certain knowledge that if he or she does pick up that˘ first drink, what will come next shouldn't happen to a dog.

The fact remains that the alcoholic must want sobriety enough to take Antabuse. To charge the problem drinker's wife or husband with the responsibility of administering the daily dose generally defeats the purpose by setting up resentments in the pill taker's mind and sometimes starting a grim game in which the alcoholic seeks to outwit the one giving the Antabuse.

As in all other forms of treatment, *the alcoholic must want sobriety!*

I've heard it said that in really bad cases, alcoholic hallucinations persist long after detoxification. Is this true?

This is a possibility that is so remote that it's not worth worrying about. Of course, the speed and extent of physical recovery varies with the individual as well as with the duration and severity of the uncontrolled drinking. But, generally speaking, hallucinations don't hang on long, if at all, following detoxification.

My problem drinker has a horror of being put in a straitjacket or given the wet binding sheet treatment if he should blow his stack during withdrawal.

Tell him to relax. With the use of modern drug therapy, the need for restraint has been reduced to the vanishing point. Patients with even the most agitated withdrawal symptoms have been found to respond much better to quiet surroundings, constant reassurances by attendants to allay hallucinatory fears, and the use of medication, than to the old lock-'em-up and tie-'em-down treatment of other years.

Again, be thankful that your problem drinker is going through the bad time in this day and age instead of twenty or twenty-five years ago, when alcoholics in withdrawal were treated pretty brutally.

Is psychotherapy a part of detoxification?

No. That may come later, during rehabilitation.

Can an alcoholic go through detoxification at home?

Yes, if the proper medication and care are assured. The alcoholic's spouse, family, and/or friends must be prepared for what amounts to round-the-clock nursing. The attending physician's cooperation is another *must* for home detoxification.

We're speaking, of course, of the very ill alcoholic. A drying-out problem drinker who is shaky but able to make it to the doctor's office may be examined there, have medication prescribed, and may be furnished with a diet to get him or her through the bad time on an out-patient basis.

If there's a drawback to this procedure, it's the busy doctor's possible or even probable failure to make the alcoholic recognize the seriousness of the situation. Too often, the alcoholic continues to operate on the theory: "Well, I can always depend on good old Doc to fix me up if the going gets rough."

Eventually, good old Doc gets fed up with this repeater and sends him or her to the hospital anyway. But there's all that time wasted that could possibly have been saved if the alcoholic had been made to face up to the worsening illness by being put in a hospital for detoxification.

Generally speaking, if the alcoholic needs medical help when coming off the sauce, such help is more efficiently administered at a hospital with far less strain on everybody concerned.

Do our hospitalization insurance policies cover treatment for alcoholism?

Some of the hospitalization policies issued these days cover costs of alcoholic detoxification under certain varying stipulations. Better check your policy or call your agent to find out the coverage extended by your policy.

Blue Cross is one of the leading medical insurance organizations which has lowered the bars against paying for detoxification treatment. If the alcoholic is a veteran of the armed forces, he can benefit from a considerably expanded alcoholism program recently instituted in veterans hospitals. The great majority of corporate medical insurance policies now include alcoholism coverage.

Many insurance companies issuing hospitalization coverage have found it more realistic to provide benefits for alcoholism patients under a factual diagnosis rather than to go through the mummery of covering these patients under phony diagnoses.

When my problem drinker comes out of the hospital, are there any Do's or Don'ts I should follow?

Probably the most important Don't is to throw any blocks in the course of rehabilitation that will be prescribed for him or her.

Remember, detoxification can be the first step in the alcoholic's recovery but only if it's followed up by rehabilitation, either in a rehab center, through expert counseling, and/or as a member of Alcoholics Anonymous.

Most patients coming out of detoxification are depressed in spite of all the assurances given them by doctors, nurses, and the AA contacts they may have made to the effect that this can be the start of something great. Perhaps your first job will be to do as much as you can to help lighten this depression, this feeling of failure, unworthiness, and a dread of the future.

Do everything possible to make sure the alcoholic follows the rehabilitation course laid down by his or her doctors. Refrain from any suggestion of reproach. Emphasize the fact that the alcoholic has been hospitalized because of a disease, not because of any moral failing. By every means possible, show the alcoholic that he or she has not lost your love.

If a stay at a rehabilitation center has been recommended, be ready to meet the almost inevitable protest: "We can't afford the money and I can't afford to lose all that time." Without bickering or acrimony, pose the question of how much it's going to cost in money and time—not to speak of confusion and misery—if the alcoholic keeps on drinking. Try to show him or her that the expenditure of a few dollars and a few weeks can't be measured against the chance for—even the probability of—a happy, meaningful future.

If we're flat-out broke and have no borrowing power, does that mean that my just-detoxified alcoholic who can't afford a rehabilitation center is up against impossible odds?

No, of course not. Always remember that Alcoholics Anonymous offers the most successful course of rehabilitation yet devised. The vast majority of rehab centers base their treatment on the AA principles. The explanation, study, and practice of these principles are available to your detoxified alcoholic at the nearest AA meeting.

Other counseling agencies are available to your detoxified problem drinker. The National Council on Alcoholism can give you information on these agencies, as can your local Mental Health Board. If you have a local Alcoholism Council, it will offer valuable rehabilitation help.

And lest you think that your problem drinker will be up against impossible odds without a stay at a rehab center, it's a fact that more men and women have found happy sobriety in AA without ever having attended a rehab center than those who have.

Then why spend the time and money to go to a rehabilitation center?

To oversimplify again, a stay at a rehabilitation center removes the newly dry alcoholic from all contact with a drinking society and its accompanying stresses for an extended period of time. He or she is surrounded by other men and women who have the same problem and is attended by professionals who know from long experience what to do and say and when to do it or say it.

The patient's physical impoverishments are tended to by doctors and dieticians who know the disease. His or her mental attitudes are brought into honest view by experienced therapists, many of whom are recovered alcoholics themselves. As a rehab center quite often is situated in a rural setting, the patient has a chance to wind down, learn how to sleep and eat again, rediscover the joys of fresh air and quiet, good food, and unregimented exercise. He or she listens to intelligent lectures and participates in stimulating rap sessions with other recovering alcoholics, led by experts skilled in drawing the true personalities out of their booze-encrusted shells.

The patient receives individual counseling as well as the support and thought-provoking action of the group session.

He or she meets some fine people—recovering alcoholics, recovered alcoholics on the staff, and even some "earth people" (nonalcoholics). He likes them, they like him; there is a rebirth of interpersonal relationships.

In many rehab centers, the emphasis is on AA. In these places, the stay constitutes a crash course in AA provided by the center's staff and by AA groups which visit the center and hold regular AA meetings there.

All in all, the person who goes to a rehabilitation center is armed with the truths about himself or herself and given the tools with which he or she can meet the problems to be faced from there on in. The alternatives to a life of sobriety are laid out—although almost never by means of horror stories. When the patient leaves the center, all self-deceptions have been stripped away, skillfully, in a kindly, considerate manner, and the recovered alcoholic is as well prepared to face the future as experience, dedication, and the accumulated knowledge of the disease of alcoholism can fit him or her.

How can I find a rehabilitation center near our home?

Your doctor may have the information you need. Attend a few open AA meetings and ask around: Chances are that you'll find a "graduate" of a convenient rehab center there. The N.C.A. information bureau is another agency you can try, or your local Mental Health Board.

Also, the Alcohol and Drug Programs Association of North America, 1130 17th Street, N.W., Washington, D.C., 20036 has published a directory of Alcoholism Treatment Facilities in the U.S. and Canada which is available to you for a small fee.

Again, may we stress the importance of planning ahead? It may seem to be negative thinking to look ahead to the time when your problem drinker will need detoxification and rehabilitation, but it's not. Things are not going to get better so long as he or she continues to drink. They can only get worse and your most affirmative moves at this point are to prepare for the inevitable so as to minimize the very real danger.

How do I contact a rehabilitation center, once I've located one?

Telephone the center or have your doctor phone. Get all the information you need, such as costs, transportation, duration of stay, and so on. *Contact two or three centers,* so that if one is full when the emergency arrives, there'll be no delay in getting the alcoholic into another. Ideally, you should arrange things so that when the problem drinker agrees to go to a rehab center, he or she will be on the way *within half an hour.*

What's the hurry?

As with all important steps in an alcoholic's recovery, time is of the essence. To give the alcoholic time to reconsider is a dangerous and sometimes fatal mistake. Remember that the alcoholic's false pride is always ready to take over again and convince the drunk that he or she can "do it on my own, one more time."

The woods (or, more correctly, the mourners' benches) are full of spouses of alcoholics who put off seeing that their problem drinkers got to a rehabilitation center without delay because of some "important engagement" they couldn't break. There's nothing more important than getting him or her into the rehab center as fast as you can, the minute he or she says, "All right, I'll go."

The seriousness of the situation must not be underestimated. Neither can the importance of getting a full fund of advance information about rehab centers, detoxification facilities, AA, or any other alcoholism agency before the crash comes. Recovered alcoholics have been trying to get this message across to nonalcoholics for years and have had to fight the general attitude of: "Maybe Joe (or Mary) will get better without needing all this."

Sir or madam, as the case might be, take the word of thousands of recovered alcoholics plus that of doctors and psychiatrists who have studied the disease of alcoholism: Your problem drinker's chances of getting better—or even living very long—without help are one in ten thousand.

And don't let anybody try to tell you different.

Helping the Alcoholic to Stay Sober and Happy

I'm realistic enough to see that if my alcoholic finds so-briety in AA or someplace else, it won't mean that the problem is solved forever, over and done with, tied up with a pink ribbon and put on a top shelf to gather dust, will it?

No, and we applaud your realistic attitude. Too often the spouse of a recovered alcoholic, particularly the husband of an alcoholic wife, affixes the stamp MISSION ACCOMPLISHED the moment the alcoholic achieves sobriety.

Always remember, alcoholism is a disease for which no cure has yet been found. Alcoholism can be arrested—hopefully for the rest of the alcoholic's life—but it will always be there, more virulent than ever if it is sprung loose again.

To the alcoholic, alcohol is a cunning, baffling, powerful, insidious, and, above all, *patient,* enemy. To paraphrase an old maxim: Eternal vigilance is the price of sobriety.

Does that mean that I've got to keep a close eye on my recovered alcoholic for the rest of my days? What's so different about my eating my heart out, worrying about him taking a drink, and what it was like before he sobered up?

No difference, if that's the way it has to be, but, of course, it doesn't—no way. Constantly looking over the alcoholic's shoulder, vocally or silently dreading a slip, is positively the worst way to play it. It's almost guaranteed to bring on a relapse.

Do you mean I'm expected to put complete faith and trust in a person who's been ripping me off all these years with lies and broken promises?

Only way to go. You've got to grasp and hold fast to the truth that it was the *sick* alcoholic who told you the lies and broke the promises. You may have trouble believing it at the start, but it's an entirely different person you'll be dealing with once the alcoholic begins the recovery process.

Of course, the transformation doesn't take place overnight but it happens faster than you might think. And the fuller your support and cooperation, the faster the arrested alcoholic's progress back into being the person he or she was intended to be.

If I don't cooperate fully, does that mean that my problem drinker will start lushing it up again?

No, not unfailingly. Plenty of alcoholics have made it without the full support of their husbands or wives, families, friends, or employers, and even against their active opposition. But it's tough and too many have fallen by the wayside who would have found a happy, sober life if they had been backed up with a little faith, trust, and loyalty.

Okay, I'll go along with that. I suppose that means I can never have another drink either, for fear of setting the alcoholic off.

Booze is the alcoholic's problem, not yours, and never is a long, long time.

When he gets on the AA program, the alcoholic learns that whether or not other people drink has nothing to do with him. He further learns how to guard against being resentful of the fact that another person (you) can drink and he can't. In time, he usually becomes entirely comfortable around social drinkers.

You'll notice that we said *in time*. At the very beginning of your alcoholic's recovery program, we'd advise going the Coke or tomato juice route with him or her, as the case might be.

However—and it's a big however—don't make a production out of it. The look-what-I'm-doing-for-your-sake attitude or the now-isn't-this-cream-soda-much-jollier-than-a-martini nonsense can be worse than getting smashed in front of the newly sober alcoholic.

We once knew the wife of a struggling recoveree whose shrill voice was raised above all others at every cocktail party they attended. "Oh, no, thanks," she would shriek.

"I'd love one but you see, Jake's an alcoholic and can't drink and I'm with him all the way, poor dear."

And, yes, there have been husbands who have been just as stupid in making things tough for their newly sober alcoholic wives.

Which brings up the question, what about cocktail parties?

It all depends on whether or not your recovered alcoholic is going to be miserable. In the beginning, we'd say send regrets and make sure you're busy doing something else, not sitting at home wishing things were different. Go out for an early dinner, go to an open AA meeting, go to the movies.

Later on, when the recoveree has some sobriety built up, he or she may be able to stand and even enjoy an occasional cocktail party. Usually, the biggest problem the nondrinking alcoholic has to face at these affairs is not an overpowering urge to drink but the fight to keep from being bored out of his or her skull. Somehow the conversation is not quite as sparkling to the one drinking ginger ale as it is to those who are drinking liquor.

Eventually, most recovered alcoholics pass up cocktail parties, not because of the drinking that's going on, but because they're so damned dull.

But if this happens to my husband (or wife), it will mean a radical change in our social life.

Uh-huh, and although you may find it hard to believe at this point, the change will be 100 percent for the better.

And we don't mean moralistically—God forbid!—but more from the standpoint of enjoyment.

That may be fine for the cocktail crowd, but my recovered alcoholic was a boilermaker drinker down at the corner tavern. All our friends hang out there. Couldn't we still go there and have him drink Coke?

There's an old saying: "If you want to stay dry, keep out of wet places."

Your ex-boilermaker drinker is working at changing his whole way of life. Even with a Coke in his hand, that's pretty impossible to do amidst the surroundings of the old way which brought both of you so much grief and woe.

And just how long do you think he'd stick to Coke?

But we'll lose all our friends!

Lady, with his sobriety, you're both going to make new friends who will make you wonder what you ever saw in the others. That's a promise. You'll both find Alcoholics Anonymous the most truly friendly fellowship on the face of the earth. And the one which has more fun than all the others put together.

Shall I keep liquor in the house or would that be too big a temptation?

It's not the temptation so much as the *availability,* at least at the start. A shaky beginner in sobriety should not have to put up with the knowledge that there's a bottle close by, his or hers for the reaching. Later on, you may keep and serve alcoholic beverages or you may not; it will depend on your own better judgment or the ex-drunk's. Some, if not most, of our AA friends keep liquor in the house and serve it to their nonalcoholic friends, but there are others whose judgment we respect equally who say absolutely not.

Whatever you do, don't fall for the old and cockeyed argument offered by some brash beginners: "I want a bottle of booze handy to prove I've got it licked."

Should we stay out of restaurants that have a bar?

While we know it's hard to find a top-flight restaurant without a bar these days, it probably will be worth the effort to find boozeless eateries during the early days of sobriety. Until the recoveree gets his or her feet on the ground and knows that life without liquor can not only be bearable but better than it ever was before, plunking him or her down with people who are having cocktails, wine, or beer with their meals, and after-dinner drinks, constitutes undue hardship. In the early stages of sobriety, such surroundings may raise the old whimper *Why can't I?* and your alcoholic might be tempted to give it one more try.

Later on, the recovered alcoholic may not give a thought to the liquor being served around him, other than occasionally reminding himself that what's okay for the non-alcoholic is deadly poison to him. But on the other hand, many sober alcoholics just don't want to be around the stuff under any circumstances.

There's an old saying in AA: "If it makes you uncomfortable, avoid it; it's dangerous to your sobriety." At times, this has meant walking out of a restaurant in the middle of a good dinner.

Do you mean that from now on my sobered-up drunk must gauge every situation he finds himself in as it relates to his sobriety?

Yes, he knows that his sobriety is the most important thing in his life and that he must go to any lengths to protect and preserve it. In the extremely rare event that he finds himself in a situation which is just too uncomfortable, creating resentments and/or self-pity, or, worst of all, bringing on the insidious urge to join the nonalcoholics for "just a couple," he must get the hell out of there.

Must we give up all our friends even though most of them are nonalcoholic one- or two-drink people?

If your recovered alcoholic is comfortable with them and if they're comfortable with him (or her), we see no reason to break off the acquaintance.

If the friends are comfortable with the recovered alcoholic? Just what do you mean by that?

It may come as a shock, but a recovered alcoholic's lifestyle usually changes so drastically—and always for the better—that common interests which once bound old friends and acquaintances fade out of sight. By this we don't mean that the recoveree adopts any holier-than-thou attitude or deliberately avoids friends who are able to drink. It's just that sobriety is his imperative interest and his recovery program requires important changes in his makeup. These old friends eventually find that they're dealing with an entirely new person and sometimes they're not comfortable with him.

In most cases, new friends with important common interests replace drinking acquaintances—even one-drink drinkers—in a gradual revision of social values. This all sounds a lot more upsetting than it really is and it takes place over an extended period of time, so don't worry about it now.

Must we give up all business, civic, and social affairs which are preceded by the so-called "Happy Hour"?

In the early days of sobriety, if you feel you really must attend the affair, arrange to arrive at the very end of the "Happy Hour."

Later on, say after ninety days' sobriety, the recovered alcoholic may want to participate, sipping a "Virgin Mary" or a "Shirley Temple." But under no circumstances should he or she attend a "Happy Hour" out of a mistaken sense of social or business obligation. It could turn out to be the unhappiest hour of his or her life.

Should I attend open AA meetings with my spouse?

The first inclination is to say, "Of course!" But a blanket statement just doesn't cover it.

In some cases, the person new to AA wants the spouse to be at his or her side in the early open meetings. In other instances, the newly sober person feels more comfortable if the spouse is not there at the very beginning.

Whichever way it is in your case, the AA's decision should be respected. A husband or wife should *never* insist on going to open meetings against the new AA's wishes.

This is where Al-Anon plays such an important role for the nonalcoholic spouse, especially when the AA is necessarily separated from him or her in a closed meeting. It's the best remedy known for that "left-out feeling."

Can the alcoholic's sex life be expected to improve with sobriety?

Everything about the alcoholic can be expected to improve with sobriety. This certainly includes his or her sex life. But don't expect an overnight return to the honeymoon days. The sick alcoholic doesn't get that much better that fast.

Will all our family and financial troubles disappear, now that my problem drinker is sober?

You didn't really expect a yes answer to that when you asked it, did you? Of course they won't. There's a lot of magic attached to a person's recovery from alcoholism, but the ability to put the immediate zap on overdue bills and all other assorted troubles isn't included.

The important thing is that with sobriety comes the ability to cope. As overwhelming as the difficulties might seem to the newly sober person, he or she is armed with a new weapon to use against them, sobriety. There's no guarantee that things won't get even tougher but now they can be faced, met, and dealt with without the crippling handicap of a head filled with booze fumes.

With sobriety comes a return of self-respect, self-confidence, courage, and faith in the future. What troubles can defeat that lineup?

How soon after sobriety can the alcoholic be expected to assume some of the responsibilities that he or she has let slide?

The word is: *Easy does it.*

Most newly dried-up alcoholics have a tendency to rush into things, wanting to repair all the damage that the years of alcoholism have wrought immediately if not sooner. Unless cooled off and calmed down, these do-it-now people may get themselves so bollixed up that they put their new-found program of living without alcohol in jeopardy.

There's no rule of thumb about how soon a recovered alcoholic should start assuming the responsibilities he or she has let slide. Some people straighten out their thinking faster than others; some are just naturally more responsibility-conscious than others; everybody's ability to procrastinate varies. It can be safely said that after that first euphoric surge of frantic fix-it rushing around, the recovered alcoholic will reassume his or her responsibilities at the pace best suited to the individual personality.

Don't worry; your recovered problem drinker wants to get back in life's mainstream as soon as he or she possibly can—but without endangering his or her program. Don't try to rush things.

Do you mean I must never prod him (or her) to get going?

Only if you're positive that the recovered alcoholic is copping out, misusing the recovery program to excuse laziness. And even then, assuming that he's in AA, it might be wise to have a few words with his sponsor before you let him have it.

Sponsor? What's a sponsor?

An AA sponsor is a man or woman with a solid program who guides the newcomer during his or her early experience in AA. The newcomer chooses the sponsor, someone he or she can relate to, somebody whose sobriety is the kind the newcomer wants for himself or herself.

The sponsor answers the questions, talks over the problems, points out the well-known danger signals. Sometimes theirs is a very close friendship, sometimes a loose association, depending on which the beginner is more comfortable with.

I've heard somewhere that when my problem drinker does go to AA, it will be up to me to keep hands off his (or her) program, even when it seems tottery. True?

Yes, to a great extent. Remember, this is the alcoholic's recovery program with everything worthwhile at stake in its success. Even the best-intentioned interference could be disastrous.

We fully realize that in something so important to you, whose hope for peace of mind, happiness, a real life with your alcoholic depends so much on the success of his or her program, it's terribly difficult to keep hands off, especially when you're afraid that it's not going right. But as you'll learn in Al-Anon, you can *never* work the program for the alcoholic. You must follow the sometimes difficult course of offering full cooperation at the same time you avoid all take-charge tendencies.

About the best thing you can do if your problem drinker is obviously going off the program is to contact his or her sponsor and let the sponsor take it from there. But do this only as a last resort. Chances are the sponsor already knows if something is really going wrong.

Is everything my spouse tells me about a closed AA meeting just between us two or can I share it with a trusted friend?

Your recovered alcoholic isn't going to tell you anything that happens in a closed AA meeting. The reason the meetings are closed to all but alcoholics is to give the participants a chance to lay it all out with the certainty that whatever they might say stops there. Period.

After putting up with Dolores (or Tom) all these years while she (or he) was out of control, can I be blamed for resenting her (his) leaving me every damned night in the week in favor of these new AA friends?

Human nature being what it is, we can't blame anybody for entertaining a sneaking feeling of resentment or even jealousy at times in the very beginning. You, who love her (or him) so much and who tried so hard to help—and failed—seem to be neglected in favor of a bunch of strangers.

This is particularly true in the case of the nonalcoholic husband. All too often, when his problem drinker finally goes to AA, he says something like, "Great, she can devote all the time she wants to her new program—within reason."

Then, when his idea of "within reason" doesn't jibe with her needs, there's trouble.

Once again, at the risk of sounding overly repetitive, let us emphasize the importance of the nonalcoholic's early and sustained contact with Al-Anon. It can make all the difference between a rough or smooth road in early sobriety for both the alcoholic and the nonalcoholic.

Suppose there is no Al-Anon group in our home town?

Then you have the heaven-sent opportunity to help start a new group. Your spouse's AA group will be glad to give you a hand in any way it can.

What should I do if my AA wife (or husband) has a slip?

Well, first of all, don't sit around waiting for her (or him) to have a slip. You have plenty of reason to accentuate the positive; hundreds of thousands of AAs have experienced no trouble from their very first contact with AA.

However, it does happen that the newcomer gets off the beam (and some old-timers, too), permits herself what is known in AA as "stinking thinking" (resentments, self-pity), and picks up that first drink. It's a shock and a strain to those most closely concerned. There's a tendency to panic, to throw up one's hands and cry, "If AA doesn't work, there's no hope."

But AA does work. It's the slipper who has temporarily abandoned AA. Perhaps it's a bad analogy because it connotes a cure, but if a person threw away a vitally necessary medicine and got sicker, who would say that the medicine didn't work?

Your job in such a case would be to get the slipper back on track and, against all your probable inclinations, this will best be done without any weeping, wailing, accusations, or threats. That wouldn't get any better results than it did before the problem drinker found AA.

Hold fast to the knowledge that she (or he) has been exposed to AA. Regardless of her twisted thinking at the time of the slip, she knows deep down that the road she's following leads nowhere but to a worse despair than she's ever experienced. She's heard stories of others who decided to go back to drinking and what happened to them. She also knows that she's got a lot of good friends waiting to give her a hand back up when she decides to quit playing Russian Roulette with her life. And be assured that her drinking is extremely joyless.

There's a saying in AA: "We might not keep you sober, but we can sure as hell ruin your drinking."

Should I call her (or his) sponsor?

Yes, but don't expect a flying squad of AAs to descend on your drinking slipper, exhorting her (or him) to straighten up and fly right. This sometimes happens—without the exhortations, of course—but at other times there might be a casual visit, a phone call, or even the silent treatment. It all depends on the individual's needs. One person might best respond to being surrounded by AA friends who give needed assurances that the door of return to AA is wide open. Another might be turned off by such "butting in." The silent treatment might deal such a blow to an inflated ego that the slipper finally realizes that AA doesn't have to have her; she has to have AA.

Again, your Al-Anon experience will prepare you for a possible slip. And one more time: Don't give thinking room to these negative ideas about a slip being inevitable. It's not. Remember those 65 percent first-time-around success statistics we gave you awhile back? They prove that your problem drinker has a much better than even chance of never experiencing any kind of trouble, once he or she goes to AA.

Are there many social activities put on by AA and will I have to endure these affairs if I'm to be a good helpmate to my recovered alcoholic?

First, let's strike out the word "endure," shall we? Perhaps we haven't stressed it enough, so let's say it again: AA is a lot of fun.

It's fairly impossible for the outsider to believe this, much less understand it, and yet all that's required to get at least an inkling of this truth is to drop in on an average AA open meeting. The men and women you'll see there won't be filling those chairs because they have to (although attendance at meetings is one of the mainstays of a successful recovery program); they'll be there because they want to be.

Not to be flippant about the grim reason for AA's existence, the fellowship's philosophy, and the unmatched accomplishments of AA, but it can be said that Alcoholics Anonymous is the longest-running hit show on record, with a cast of characters you wouldn't believe unless you saw and heard them.

These people have learned to live life a day at a time, adhering to principles that give them a chance to live that life to its fullest, and one of the first joys they reclaim in their recovery program is the ability to laugh—at themselves. Because there is no competition in AA, they can hang loose. They never need to put up a front. Nobody will criticize them for any faults that may still cling to them as they work to correct them. Nobody wears a halo in recognition of good deeds well done. There is no seniority; the twenty-year gal is no more important in the AA group than the newcomer with forty-eight hours of sobriety—perhaps not as important because the group conscience is directed toward helping the newcomer in the early stages.

And over everything else hangs the spirit of true friendship and high good humor. In most members' opinions, it is impossible to duplicate this spirit in any other organization known to man. These people have been way down, about as far down as you can go and still survive. They've been given a chance not only to live but to enjoy life as they never dreamed possible. Is it any wonder that they laugh a lot?

Then AA is an intensely personal experience?

Alcoholics Anonymous is both a personal and an impersonal experience. This might be a little hard to explain, but let's give it a try.

When the newcomer goes to AA, he or she naturally

forms a personal attachment to the men and women in the group. They welcome the newcomer, they offer aid and understanding, they become personal friends.

As the newcomer widens the scope of AA experience to include other groups, he or she finds that the same understanding friendship exists there, too. The newcomer makes new friends outside the home group and the program is depersonalized a bit, but without weakening any of the first fine attachments.

Then comes the time when the AA member finds himself in a strange city, on vacation or a business trip or whatever. He attends a meeting where he doesn't know a soul. He's given the same friendly welcome he'd give an out-of-town visitor to his own home group, but this is strictly a dropping in and the next day he moves on. Still, without participating in the meeting beyond listening, he has bolstered his recovery program by having made contact with AA on an entirely impersonal basis.

Most successful AAs agree that a member needs both personal and impersonal AA. The first is necessary and precious. But to be sure that there will never be a time when the individual's program might suffer because the personal contacts are unavailable, the AA should prepare himself or herself to rely on the vast, impersonal strength of AA that is ready to serve at any time, anywhere the recovered alcoholic goes.

You never did answer that question about AA social affairs.

Some AA groups throw a lot of parties of one kind or another and some don't. There are hundreds of AA-oriented clubhouses scattered throughout the land, having no official connection with Alcoholics Anonymous but providing places where AAs can hold meetings, throw parties, or just drop in to shoot the breeze with other AAs over a cup of the best coffee in town.

There are regular state, area, and national conventions which are high points in warm fellowship, as well as business meetings where things actually get done at morning sessions (no hangovers). Usually three-day affairs held at some of the nation's most posh watering places, their attraction is best proved by the fact that reservations are invariably oversubscribed and AAs come from all over to be there, usually at their own expense.

When the convention banquet hall is full and the gavel ready to sound, somebody is always sure to say, "Can you imagine what kind of a scene this would be if we were all still drinking?"

TEN

How to Handle the Alcoholic Employee

Just how big is the problem of the alcoholic employee?

Would you call $15 billion a year big?

That's what alcoholic employees are costing U.S. business and industry each year. Of this total $10 billion represents the work hours lost because of alcoholism—the hours that the alcoholic can't work because he's drunk or hung over. The other $5 billion takes in losses due to poor work performance, alcohol-induced accidents, product rejects, and so forth.

Never mind the big picture: How many drunks would you estimate are on my *payroll?*

Approximately 5 percent of the average payroll are alcoholics. Another 5 percent abuse alcohol to the extent that their work suffers badly from time to time, usually with increasing frequency.

Why not fire them all and be done with the problem?

Easier said than done, even if you really wanted to swing the ax so recklessly. First, they're awfully hard to find. Alcoholics are master con artists and they're at their best (or worst, depending on your point of view) when they're hiding their problem from higher-ups. Second, as previously noted, fellow employees cover for them rather than risk the dreaded label of ratfink. If there is no company policy on rehabilitating alcoholic employees, union shop stewards will go to any lengths to keep a union man from being bounced for drinking. Furthermore, the alcoholic somehow seems able to turn in a marginal performance long past the time when he should be removed from his desk or bench for the good of everybody concerned. Lastly, and perhaps most important to you as the employer, more than half these alcoholics are in key positions and hard to replace.

How do I go about recognizing the alcoholics on my payroll?

By work performance alone. It's the only realistic Geiger counter to use. A man or woman's absenteeism, accident record, erratic behavior, poor production rate, and an increasing frequency of bad decisions are all signs of a worker who may be suffering from alcoholism.

Are you trying to tell me that every employee who performs poorly, behaves erratically, and is frequently absent is an alcoholic?

Not every one—but at least half of them are.

What about the other half?

Chances are they're having marital problems, they're on drugs, or they're sick from something other than alcoholism.

Okay, what should I do about the problem?

First, you can establish a company policy under which alcoholism is defined as an illness, with employees suffering from the disease of alcoholism being handled exactly as employees stricken with any other illness.

Second, establish a "third party" counselor, a man or woman trained in counseling alcoholics, either as part of your medical department or in an extramural office. An alcoholic employee is sent to this counselor by his supervisor, or, in the case of a high-ranking executive, by you yourself, always with a full guarantee of confidentiality.

How does the supervisor approach the suspected alcoholic?

Very carefully. Something like: "Look, Joe, your work is falling off badly. I don't want to write a poor report on you unless I have to. Something is bugging you and I can't help you anymore, so go see Dr. Jones in the medical office."

So the medical officer tells him he's an alcoholic. What then?

The employee is referred to further counseling, to AA, and/or to an alcoholic rehabilitation center.

What if he won't go?

Fire him for poor work performance.

Does a recovered alcoholic perform satisfactorily when he or she comes back to work after a stay in a rehab center?

At least as well as before things got bad and usually much better.

If I have an employee who has just found sobriety, should I change his job if it includes taking customers out to lunch or dinner or an occasional night on the town?

You'll be giving him a big hand up if you let somebody else substitute for him in the entertaining department, at least during his first ninety days in AA—and possibly for keeps.

However, we think it's important that the newly sober employee be given your assurances that this change in duties in no way reflects on his overall job effectiveness.

Of the alcoholic employees who accept help, how many straighten up and fly right?

Sixty-five percent find sobriety in their first attempt. About 75 percent make it by the end of the first year.

What if the alcoholic employee starts drinking again?

He or she deserves a second chance, perhaps a third. But if it develops the alcoholic is playing funny games, fire him or her for poor work performance.

Can you give me the names of some companies that have used this approach successfully?

The list is a long one but a few companies that might be mentioned are: Merrill Lynch, Pierce, Fenner, and Smith; American Airlines; E. I. Dupont De Nemours & Co., Inc.; Eastman Kodak Company; Kemper Insurance; Hughes Aircraft; Kennecott Copper Corporation; and Consolidated Edison Company of New York, Inc. This admittedly is skimming the surface. We just haven't room to list even a representative group of big corporations and smaller companies which have proved the invaluable worth of alcoholism programs within their work forces.

What about unions?

The old union policy of "protect the member's job at any cost" is pretty much a thing of the past as concerns the alcoholic union man or woman. Nowadays, most unions are enthusiastically cooperating with management in identifying and offering help to the alcoholic employee. A big part of the program's success depends on the supervisor in making the first approach to the alcoholic. Experience has proved that even reluctant and suspicious unions lost their indifferent or antagonistic viewpoints once the details of the alcoholism program were spelled out for them.

Where can I get specific information on these matters?

Write The Conference Board, Inc., at 845 Third Avenue, New York, New York, 10022. Ask for the publication "Company Controls for Drinking Problems."

For Your Information

Alcoholics Anonymous: See your local telephone directory or write to: A.A. General Service Office, Grand Central Station, Post Office Box 459, New York, New York 10017.

Al-Anon: Contact through your local AA telephone listing or write to: Al-Anon Family Groups, Post Office Box 182, Madison Square Station, New York, New York 10010.

National Council on Alcoholism, 2 Park Avenue, New York, New York 10016.

National Institute on Alcoholism and the Abuse of Alcohol, Clearing House for Alcohol Information, Post Office Box 2345, Rockville, Maryland, 20852.

Alcohol and Drug Programs Association of North America, 1130 17th St., N.W., Washington, D.C. 20036. Publishers of Alcoholism Treatment Facilities Directory (1973–1974), United States and Canada.

DATE DUE

JAN 1 2 '76	DE 4 '84		
FEB 13 '76	DE 5 '85		
MAR 12 '76	JY 21 '87		
APR 1 '76	NO 21 '87		
JUL 15 '76	FE 5 '88		
AUG 23 '76	JY 28 88		
Sept 7	FE 7 '89		
DEC 1 '77	MY 15 '89		
FEB 3 '78	SE 29 '89		
MAR 3 '78	MAY 17		
FEB 5 '79	MAR 30 '93		
MAY 10 '79	NOV 15 '93		
May 24	NOV 30 '93		
JUN 7 '79	DEC 14 '93		
NOV 13	OCT 3 '94		
JUN 3 '80	SEP 1 '95		
FEB 16	DEC 04		
FE 2 '84			
GAYLORD			PRINTED IN U.S.A.